Maths

The 11+ Practice Book

with Assessment Tests

For the CEM (Durham University) test

Ages
10-11

Practise • Prepare • Pass

Everything your child needs for 11+ success

How to use this Practice Book

This book is divided into two parts — themed question practice and full-length assessment tests. There are answers and detailed explanations in the pull-out section at the back of the book.

Themed question practice

- Each page contains practice questions divided by topic. Use these pages to work out your child's strengths and the areas they find tricky. The questions get harder down each page.

Assessment tests

- The second part of the book contains four full-length assessment tests, each with a mix of question types from the first part of the book. They take a similar form to the maths sections of the real test.

- You can print off multiple-choice answer sheets from our website, www.cgplearning.co.uk/11+, so your child can practise taking the tests as if they're sitting the real thing.

- If you want to give your child timed practice, give them a time limit of 35 minutes for each test, and ask them to work as quickly and carefully as they can.

- Your child should aim for a mark of around 85% (51 questions correct) in each test. If they score less than this, use their results to work out the areas they need more practice on.

- If they haven't managed to finish the test in time, they need to work on increasing their speed, whereas if they have made a lot of mistakes, they need to work more carefully.

- Keep track of your child's scores using the progress chart on the inside back cover of the book.

Published by CGP

Editors:
Rachel Grocott, Shaun Harrogate, Paul Jordin, Rachael Rogers and Sophie Scott

Contributors:
Stephanie Burton, Susan Foord, Julie Hunt, Katrina Saville

With thanks to Sharon Keeley-Holden, Sarah Oxley and Rachel Murray for the proofreading.

Please note that CGP is not associated with CEM or The University of Durham in any way.
This book does not include any official questions and it is not endorsed by CEM or The University of Durham.
CEM, Centre for Evaluation and Monitoring, Durham University and *The University of Durham*
are all trademarks of The University of Durham.

ISBN: 978 1 84762 561 8
www.cgpbooks.co.uk
Printed by Elanders Ltd, Newcastle upon Tyne
Clipart from Corel®

Based on the classic CGP style created by Richard Parsons.

CONTENTS

Place Value

For each row of numbers below, circle the number that has the smallest value.

1. 2076   2109   10 102   1979   2000

2. 1.06   6.15   15.06   10.56   100.50

3. 475.5   54.75   7.55   7.09   15.01

4. 980.1   974.8   98.01   98.45   98.1

5. 0.946   0.878   1.811   1.02   0.923

Copy out the numbers below, and add a decimal point so that each number has 5 tens.

Example: 35982 | 3 | 5 | 9 | . | 8 | 2 |

6. 62520

7. 51303

8. 7541

9. 210522

10. 325781

Hint: The tens column is two places to the left of the decimal point:
Th H T U . tenths

Write down the number each arrow is pointing to.

11.   35 ——————— 85

12.   40 ——————— 60

13.   5.8 ——————— 5.9

14. Stacey wrote down the heights, in feet (ft), of five mountains in Europe.
    Circle which one is the tallest.

    A 11 227 ft   **B** 11 293 ft   **C** 10 991 ft   **D** 11 112 ft   **E** 11 242 ft

15. Which of these pairs of numbers are the same distance from 14? Circle the answer.

    A 13.74 and 14.36   **C** 14.61 and 13.49   **E** 14.4 and 13.8

    B 13.82 and 14.18   **D** 13.33 and 14.33

/ 5

Rounding Up and Down

Circle each correctly rounded answer.

1.	6726 to the nearest 100	6720	6800	6700	7000	6730
2.	9345 to the nearest 10	9340	9346	9350	9400	9300
3.	64.77 to the nearest whole number	65	65.70	60	64	64.7
4.	0.287 to the nearest hundredth	0.29	0.30	0.20	0.289	0.299
5.	1095.93 to the nearest 100	1096	1100	1090	1105	1000

/ 5

Round 4990.63 to:

6. the nearest 10.

7. the nearest 1000.

8. the nearest tenth.

9. the nearest whole number.

10. the nearest 100.

/ 5

11. Which of these is equal to 2400? Circle the correct answer.

A 2351 rounded to the nearest 1000
B 2347 rounded to the nearest 100
C 2356 rounded to the nearest 10
D 2389 rounded to the nearest 10
E 2439 rounded to the nearest 100

12. Round 36.572 kg to the nearest 100 g.

 kg

13. A newspaper reports that there were 45 500 people at a football match.
This number has been rounded to the nearest 100.
What is the fewest number of people that could
have been at the football match?

14. Josie measures the length of the school field as 125.639 m.
How long is the field to the nearest 10 cm?
Give your answer in metres.

 m

15. The population of a city is 437 985.
What is the population of the city to the nearest 10 000?

/ 5

Section One — Working with Numbers

Addition

Write down the answer to each calculation.

1. 72 + 56

2. 135 + 258

3. 268 + 945

4. 567 + 2645

5. 1076 + 1177

6. 3303 + 4868

Write down the answer to each calculation.

7. 9.3 + 3.5

8. 6.2 + 17.8

9. 34.23 + 22.73

Hint: If you use the column method for these questions, remember to line up the decimal points.

10. 25.7 + 24.5

11. 11.23 + 4.58

/ 11

12. Jasmine and Tom went to the sweet shop. Jasmine bought a chocolate bar for 38p and a carton of orange juice for 64p. Tom bought a banana for 32p and bubblegum for 29p. How much did they spend in total?

£ [ ][ ] . [ ][ ]

The Quick Café menu is shown on the right.

13. Mrs White buys a bacon roll and a tea from the Quick Café. How much does she spend?

£ [ ][ ] . [ ][ ]

Quick Café Menu	
Bacon roll	£1.45
Toast and jam	£1.25
Full breakfast	£1.85
Tea	75p
Coffee	85p

14. Mr Brown stopped for a snack at the Quick Café and spent exactly £3.55. Which items did he buy? Circle the answer.

  A   Bacon roll, full breakfast
  B   Full breakfast, toast and jam, tea
  C   Full breakfast, coffee
  D   Bacon roll, toast and jam, coffee
  E   Full breakfast, tea

15. Farrah posts four parcels weighing 24.5 kg, 16.2 kg, 6.25 kg and 5.4 kg. What is the total weight of these parcels?

[ ][ ] . [ ] kg

16. Julie bought a washing machine for £490.90, a vacuum cleaner for £55.50 and a coffee machine for £127.20. How much did she spend in total?

£ [ ][ ][ ] . [ ][ ]

/ 5

Subtraction

Write down the answer to each calculation.

Hint: Partitioning is a good way of tackling subtraction calculations.

1. 56 – 32

2. 84 – 29

3. 1062 – 358

4. 264.3 – 82.5

5. 13.2 – 4.16

Fill in the missing number in each of the following calculations:

6. 42 – ☐☐ = 31

7. 5.3 – ☐☐☐ = 2.1

8. 124 – ☐☐ = 52

9. 17.4 – ☐☐☐ = 9.8

10. 664 – ☐☐☐ = 406

11. 25.6 – ☐☐☐☐☐ = 19.46

/ 11

12. Shefali baked 48 cakes. She decorated 12 with chocolate icing, 15 with lemon, 6 with orange, 9 with strawberry and the rest with coffee icing. How many cakes were decorated with coffee icing?

13. 60 children went on a school trip. The coach dropped them off at different places on the way home. Patrick recorded the number of children who got off at each point. Church Avenue was the last stop, so everyone left on the bus got off. How many children got off at Church Avenue?

Bus Stop	Number who got off the bus
Creek Street	15
Exeter Street	7
New Street	4
Crompton Road	9
Market Square	14
Church Avenue	

14. Mr Reid had a plank of wood which was 320 cm long. On Monday he cut off 120 cm of wood from the plank. On Tuesday he cut off 63 cm. On Wednesday he cut off another 66 cm. How long was the remaining plank of wood? ☐☐ cm

Rona and Jenny went to the newsagents. Rona spent £2.60 on a comic and £1.22 on a birthday card. Jenny bought a magazine for £3.20 and a bottle of water for 75p.

15. Rona paid for her things with a £10 note. How much change did she get? £ ☐☐.☐☐

16. How much more did Jenny spend than Rona? ☐☐ p

/ 5

Section One — Working with Numbers

Multiplying and Dividing by 10, 100 and 1000

Write down the answer to each calculation.

1. 12×100

2. 3.6×1000

3. 0.24×10

4. 169.454×100

5. 0.062×1000

Write down the answer to each calculation.

6. $3472 \div 100$

7. $94.6 \div 10$

8. $48.3 \div 100$

9. $0.46 \div 10$

10. $3205 \div 1000$

/ 10

11. $4720 = 100 \times$ ____
    What is the missing number? Circle the correct answer.
    A   472   B   47.2   C   47   D   47 200   E   47 200

12. Martin is making a scale model of his school. He measures
    the length of the actual science block as 2240 cm. He wants
    his model to be 100 times smaller than the real building.
    How long should his model science block be?

    cm

13. A pack of 10 pens costs £2.70.   A box of pens contains
    100 packs. Mrs Chapman buys 10 boxes of pens.
    How much does this cost?

    £

14. The population of Ampney is 10 times larger than the population of Bentley.
    The population of Bentley is 1000 times smaller than the population of Clifton.
    The population of Clifton is 10 times larger than the population of Dannett.
    If the population of Ampney is 2630, what is the population of Dannett?

    / 4

Section One — Working with Numbers

Multiplication

Write down the answer to each calculation.

1. 13 × 8

2. 9 × 24

3. 17 × 14

4. 330 × 5

5. 65 × 22

6. 47 × 16

Write down the answer to each calculation.

7. 3.6 × 6

8. 4.2 × 7

9. 9.3 × 8

10. 6.4 × 70

11. 2.2 × 12

12. 0.23 × 5

/ 12

The swimming prices for Wellbeck Swimming Baths are shown in the table.

13. How much would it cost for 4 children to go swimming?   £ ☐☐ . ☐☐

14. How much would it cost for 5 adults to go swimming?   £ ☐☐ . ☐☐

	Swimming Prices
Adult	£2.30
Child	£1.95

15. On Tuesday 50 adults and 80 children went swimming. How much money did the swimming pool take on Tuesday?   £ ☐☐☐ . ☐☐

16. | 3.24 × 52 = 168.48 |

    What is 32.4 × 5.2?

17. What is 7.7 × 6.4? Circle the correct answer.

    A   62.74   **B**   38.56   **C**   0.532   **D**   49.28   **E**   4.86

    Hint: Use rounding to estimate the answer.

Charlie and Shaznay are given books to read for their homework.
Their teacher tells them how many pages they each have to read per night.

18. Charlie reads every night for three weeks. How many pages does he read in this time?

	Pages per night
Charlie	9
Shaznay	7

19. It takes Shaznay 2.5 minutes to read a page. How many minutes in total will it take her to read a book that is 90 pages long?   ☐☐☐☐☐ minutes

20. | 268 × 94 = 25 192 |

    What is 268 × 188?

/ 8

Multiplication

Circle the correct answer to each of the following questions:

21. Which calculation has the largest value?

    A 6×4000 **B** 70×300 **C** 200×200 **D** 900×10 **E** 8×500

22. Which calculation has the smallest value?

    A 4.82×0.06 **B** 2.41×0.06 **C** 2.41×0.12 **D** 4.82×0.12 **E** 9.64×0.06

23. Which calculation has the largest value?

    A 52.7×0.8 **B** 0.527×80 **C** 5.27×800 **D** 527×0.8 **E** 5270×0.008

24. $241 \times 32 = 7712$
    Which of the calculations below is incorrect?

    A $241 \times 8 = 7712 \div 4$ **D** $241 \times 33 = 7712 + 241$

    B $241 \times 64 = 7712 \times 2$ **E** $241 \times 4 = 7712 \div 16$

    C $241 \times 16 = 7712 \div 2$ **F** $241 \times 31 = 7712 - 241$

    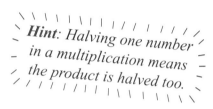
    Hint: Halving one number in a multiplication means the product is halved too.

25. If the answers to the following calculations were put in size order from smallest to largest, which would be in the middle?

    A 47×256 **B** 4.7×2.56 **C** 0.47×2.56 **D** 47×25.6 **E** 4.7×25.6

    / 5

26. Paula is buying 24 Star-Choc bars from the supermarket.
    How should Paula buy the chocolate bars to get them for the
    lowest cost? Circle the correct answer.

Star-Choc Bars
• 52p each
• Pack of 4 for £1.99
• Pack of 6 for £2.99
• Pack of 12 for £4.99
• Pack of 20 for £10.00

    A all individual bars   **C** packs of 6   **E** a pack of 20 and

    B packs of 4   **D** packs of 12   4 individual bars

27. Betty, Dave and Lorna collect stickers. Betty has 26 stickers in her collection.
    Dave has 7 times as many stickers as Betty. Lorna has 3 times as many as Betty.
    How many stickers do the three children have all together?

28. 40 bags of grain, each weighing 12.5 kg, have a total weight of 500 kg.
    What would the total weight be of 80 bags weighing 25 kg each?

     kg

29. Mr and Mrs Greengrass are both losing weight. On average
    Mr Greengrass is losing 0.27 kg a week. Mrs Greengrass is
    losing weight three times faster than Mr Greengrass.
    How much weight will Mrs Greengrass have lost after 6 weeks?

     kg

    / 4

Division

Write down the answer to each calculation.

1. $96 \div 6$

2. $124 \div 4$

3. $720 \div 5$

4. $315 \div 7$

5. $856 \div 8$

6. $67.2 \div 3$

Write down the remainder in each calculation.

7. $37 \div 5$ remainder

8. $103 \div 4$ remainder

9. $126 \div 8$ remainder

10. $186 \div 9$ remainder

11. $244 \div 8$ remainder

12. $365 \div 7$ remainder

/ 12

13. Year 6 are going on a trip. There are 81 children and 10 members of staff. How many 7-seater minibuses do they need to hire?

14. Sunita has a 560 cm length of ribbon. She cuts it into 8 equal pieces. How long, in centimetres, is each piece?   cm

15. Claire has 139 pencil sharpeners. She packs them into boxes of 8. How many boxes will she need?

Mr Bond is setting out chairs for the school assembly.

16. He can fit 9 chairs in each row. How many complete rows will he be able to make with 300 chairs?

17. 290 pupils attend the assembly. Mr Bond hands out song books and tells the pupils they must share one book between three.
    How many song books does Mr Bond need to hand out so that there's a maximum of three pupils to a book?

18. Mrs Revitt has 128 photos to put up on the display board in rows. She wants there to be the same number of photos in each row. How many photos should she put in each row to make sure she has no photos left over? Circle the correct answer.

    A   3
    B   4
    C   5
    D   6
    E   7

/ 6

Mixed Calculations

Write down the answer to each calculation.

1. $7 + 4 \times 6 - 3$ ☐☐☐☐

2. $6 + 8 \div 2 - 1$ ☐☐☐☐

3. $7 + 6 - 5 \times 2$ ☐☐☐☐

4. $9 \times 5 + 6 \times 3$ ☐☐☐☐

5. $3 \times 5 + 15 \div 5$ ☐☐☐☐

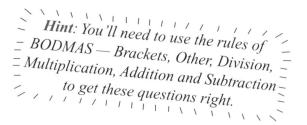

Hint: You'll need to use the rules of BODMAS — Brackets, Other, Division, Multiplication, Addition and Subtraction to get these questions right.

Complete each calculation using a +, −, × or ÷ sign.

6. $7 \boxed{} (6 + 4) = 70$

7. $9 \boxed{} (3 \times 2) = 3$

8. $3 \boxed{} (8 \times 1) = 11$

9. $27 \boxed{} (11 - 2) = 3$

10. $(4 \boxed{} 5) + 1 = 21$

11. $(9 \boxed{} 3) + 11 = 17$

/ 11

12. There are 296 pupils in Mr Charles' year group. He is printing off some worksheets for the summer term. Each pupil needs a set of 89 worksheets and an 11 page answer booklet. How many sheets of paper does Mr Charles need?
    Circle the correct answer.

    A 42 560   **B** 2344   **C** 29 600   **D** 39 200   **E** 58 080

13. Which calculation has the largest value? Circle the correct answer.

    A $7 + 6 - 4 \times 3$ **C** $7 - 6 + 4 \times 3$ **E** $7 + 6 \times 4 - 3$

    B $7 \times 6 - 4 + 3$ **D** $7 \times 6 + 4 - 3$ **F** $4 \times 6 + 7 - 3$

14. Mike wants to work out how much it will cost for his family to go to the cinema. They need tickets for 2 adults, 1 student, 3 children and 2 seniors. Circle the option below which will complete this calculation to find the total cost of the tickets:

Ticket Prices	
Adult	£4.95
Child	£2.95
Student	£3.95
Senior	£3.95

    $3 \times £3 + 3 \times £4 + 2 \times £5$ _____

    $+ 40p$ $- 40p$ $- 60 p$ $+ 50p$ $+ 60p$

15. Which calculation has the smallest value? Circle the correct answer.

    A $60 - 20 + 10 \div 5$ **C** $60 + 20 - 10 \div 5$ **E** $60 \div 20 + 10 - 5$

    B $60 - 20 \div 10 + 5$ **D** $60 + 20 \div 10 - 5$

16. What is $420 \div (60 \times 3.5)$? ☐☐☐

/ 5

Types of Number

Circle the number which has the smallest value in each list.

1.   -3   -1.5   0   0.2   2.1

2.   -2   3.6   3.06   -2.1   3.66

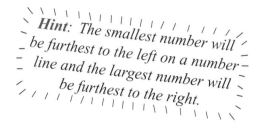

Hint: The smallest number will be furthest to the left on a number line and the largest number will be furthest to the right.

Circle the number which has the largest value in each list.

3.   -5   3.4   0   0.05   -4.2

4.   7   -5.15   7.6   0.77   -7.6

5.   Circle the highest temperature.

   -27 °C   -15 °C   -1 °C   -8 °C   -2 °C

Complete each calculation using a <, > or = sign.

Hint: Remember, < means 'less than', and > means 'greater than'.

6.   -8 ☐ 5

7.   -4 + 2 ☐ 2

8.   -2 + 6 ☐ 7 – 3

9.   -7 + 1 ☐ 5 – 13

/ 9

10. What is the sum of the even numbers between 1 and 11?   ☐☐

11. What is the sum of the odd numbers between 20 and 26?   ☐☐

12. How many whole numbers under 10 will go in the shaded area on the Venn diagram?

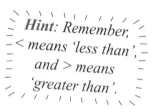

Even Numbers   Prime Numbers

☐

13. Feroz's age in years is a square number. His younger brother's age in years is also a square number. The sum of their ages is 20 years. How old is Feroz?   ☐☐

14. What is the lowest positive whole number that will go into the 'Not Prime' and 'Not Square' section of the sorting diagram?

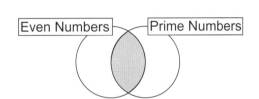

	Square	Not Square
Prime		
Not Prime		

☐☐

15. The temperature in five cities is shown in the table. What is the difference between the highest and the lowest temperatures?

 °C

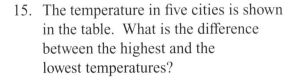

City	Temperature
Cairo	12 °C
Frankfurt	0 °C
Helsinki	-13 °C
London	2 °C
Paris	-1 °C

/ 6

Factors, Multiples and Primes

1. Circle the set of numbers which are factors of 16.

    1, 2, 3, 4, 6, 8, 16   1, 2, 6, 8, 16   1, 2, 3, 6, 16   1, 2, 4, 8, 16   1, 2, 4, 6, 16

2. Circle the set of numbers which contains all the factors of 45.

    1, 3, 5, 9, 15, 45   1, 5, 9, 45   1, 3, 5, 9, 45   1, 3, 5, 7, 15, 45   1, 3, 9, 15, 45

3. Circle the number which is a factor of both 20 and 32.

    16   4   10   8   5

4. Circle the set of numbers which contains only multiples of 3 or 4.

    3, 10, 12   4, 8, 10   15, 18, 22   12, 15, 16   20, 25, 30

5. Circle the number which is exactly divisible by both 6 and 9.

    12   18   27   30   45

/ 5

Find the highest common factor for each of these sets of numbers.

6. 16, 24, 32

8. 60, 72

7. 8, 16, 32

9. 96, 128

Find the lowest common multiple for each of these sets of numbers.

10. 5, 7

12. 2, 6, 12

11. 4, 6, 8

13. 2, 4, 5

Write these numbers as products of prime factors.

14. 15   ☐ × ☐

16. 12   ☐ × ☐ × ☐

15. 18   ☐ × ☐ × ☐

17. 36   ☐ × ☐ × ☐ × ☐

/ 12

18. What is the smallest square number
     which has both 2 and 5 as factors?

19. What is the smallest square number
     which has both 3 and 6 as factors?

/ 2

Section Two — Number Knowledge

Factors, Multiples and Primes

20. Lucy's kitten miaows every 6 seconds. Olivia's kitten miaows every 9 seconds. If they both start miaowing at the same time, after how many seconds will they next miaow again at the same time? ☐☐ seconds

21. Anna is holding a party for six children. She buys cupcakes which come in boxes of four. The children eat all the cupcakes and they all get the same number. What is the fewest number of boxes that Anna could have bought?

Hint: Use your knowledge of common multiples for questions 20 to 23.

☐☐ boxes

Emma is planting rows of seeds.
In the first row, she places beetroot seeds 9 cm apart.
In the second row, she places carrot seeds 10 cm apart.
In the third row, she places lettuce seeds 15 cm apart.
The first seeds in the three rows are in line.

beetroot ◉—9 cm—◉—9 cm—◉
carrot ◉—10 cm—◉
lettuce ◉—15 cm—◉

22. After what distance will a beetroot seed be in line with a lettuce seed again? ☐☐☐ cm

23. After what distance will all three types of seed be in line again? ☐☐☐ cm

24. Imogen has 56 sweets and 72 chocolate bars. If she wants to give an equal number of sweets and an equal number of chocolate bars to a group of friends, what is the largest number of friends she can have in the group?

Hint: Use what you have learnt about highest common factors to answer question 24.

☐☐ friends

25. Which number has been placed in the wrong section of the Venn diagram?

Multiples of 3 | Prime Numbers
9   3   7
12
8
Factors of 24

☐☐

26. Brian is thinking of a number. The number is the sum of 4 square numbers which are also factors of 64. What is the number?

Hint: Work out the factors of 64 and then see which ones are square numbers.

☐☐☐

/ 7

Fractions

Find:

1. $\frac{1}{2}$ of 12 ☐☐
2. $\frac{1}{3}$ of 9 ☐☐
3. $\frac{2}{8}$ of 8 ☐☐
4. $\frac{2}{6}$ of 24 ☐☐
5. $\frac{3}{4}$ of 36 ☐☐
6. $\frac{4}{5}$ of 45 ☐☐

/ 6

Circle the largest amount in each pair given below.

7. $\frac{1}{4}$ of 32 — $\frac{1}{3}$ of 27
8. $\frac{2}{3}$ of 33 — $\frac{1}{5}$ of 100
9. $\frac{2}{5}$ of 25 — $\frac{1}{2}$ of 18
10. $\frac{4}{5}$ of 35 — $\frac{5}{6}$ of 30
11. $\frac{1}{3}$ of 120 — $\frac{7}{8}$ of 48
12. $\frac{6}{11}$ of 88 — $\frac{7}{9}$ of 72

/ 6

13. Mrs Osborne has 8 apples to share equally between 12 children. What fraction of a whole apple should she give to each child? Circle the correct answer.

A $\frac{7}{9}$ **B** $\frac{2}{3}$ **C** $\frac{3}{4}$ **D** $\frac{6}{7}$ **E** $\frac{3}{5}$

14. The diagram shows Phoebe's kitchen floor.
What fraction of the floor is shaded? Circle the correct answer.

A $\frac{3}{8}$ **B** $\frac{1}{3}$ **C** $\frac{3}{4}$ **D** $\frac{1}{2}$ **E** $\frac{3}{5}$

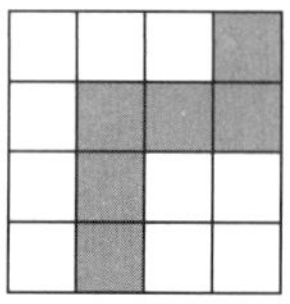

15. Josh has £4.50. He gives $\frac{1}{5}$ to his sister, $\frac{2}{9}$ to his friend, and he keeps the rest for himself. How much money does he keep?

£ ☐.☐☐

16. Martha has some marbles. She gives $\frac{2}{5}$ of them to Joseph.
Martha now has 12 marbles left.
How many marbles did Martha have to start with?

☐☐ marbles

17. Aarti wants to buy 4 dog chews. What is the difference in the price of 4 dog chews from these two shops?

Dog Empire
Dog chews.
£1 each.
Buy one get one half price!

Dog Shop
Dog chews.
£1.20 each.
Buy 3 or more and save $\frac{1}{3}$ on the total price!

£ ☐.☐☐

/ 5

Ratio and Proportion

1. Jimmy has a bag of apples. For every 3 red apples, there are 9 green apples. What is the ratio of red apples to green apples in Jimmy's bag? Write your answer in its simplest form.

    ☐ : ☐

Gabriel is making a spiced fruit cake.
The recipe says to use one part ginger to three parts cinnamon.

2. Gabriel adds 5 g of ginger. How much cinnamon should he add?

    ☐☐.☐☐ g

3. Lara makes another cake using the same recipe and adds 22.5 g of cinnamon. How much ginger does she need to add?

    ☐☐.☐☐ g

4. Amelia went pond dipping with her class. She drew a pie chart to show how many frogs and newts she found. What ratio of frogs to newts did she find in the pond? Write your answer in its simplest form.

    newts

    frogs

    ☐ : ☐

5. Nick is counting birds in a wood. His guidebook says out of every four birds he sees, he can expect one of them to be a robin. If Nick sees 32 birds, how many can he expect to be robins?

    ☐☐ robins

6. Melissa keeps rabbits. 2 out of every 3 of her rabbits are ginger. The rest are black. Melissa has 6 ginger rabbits. How many black rabbits does she have?

    ☐ black rabbits

7. For every 3 racing computer games that Joey owns, he has 5 football games. He has 6 racing games. How many games does he have in total?

    ☐☐ games

Divide the following numbers in the given ratios.

8. 500 in the ratio 3:2   ☐☐☐ : ☐☐☐

9. 420 in the ratio 4:3   ☐☐☐ : ☐☐☐

10. 640 in the ratio 5:3   ☐☐☐ : ☐☐☐

11. Elise raised £240 from her sponsored swim. She divided it in the ratio 5:4:3 between 3 charities. How much more money will the charity that receives the most get than the charity that receives the least?

    £ ☐☐☐

    / 11

Section Two — Number Knowledge

Percentages, Fractions and Decimals

1. 29% of Sara's class like spiders. What is 29% as a fraction?
    Write your answer in its simplest form.

2. Reuben gives $3/20$ of his sweets to Coralie.
    Write $3/20$ as a decimal.

3. $31/50$ of the people who live in Grizehill own
    a sheep. Write $31/50$ as a percentage.

46% of Ed's friends own a dog.

4. What is 46% as a fraction?
    Write your answer in its simplest form.

5. If Ed has 50 friends, how many of them own a dog?

/ 5

Find the following amounts.

6. 10% of 70

7. 25% of 12

8. 2% of 6400

9. 30% of 80

/ 4

10. What percentage of this shape is not shaded?

%

11. The price of a football has been reduced by 20% in a sale.
     Before the sale it cost £10.50. What is the reduced price of the football?   £

12. Mr Parkinson has 30 rose bushes in his garden. 40% of them have red
     flowers, $1/6$ of them have yellow flowers, and the rest have white flowers.
     How many of Mr Parkinson's rose bushes have white flowers?

bushes

13. The table shows how pupils in Class 6B at
     Park Rise School get to school each day.
     What percentage of the pupils travel by bus?

Type of Transport	Number of Pupils
Walk	10
Bicycle	4
Bus	12
Car	4

%

/ 4

Section Two — Number Knowledge

Algebra

If $a = 6$, work out the values of the following expressions.

1. $a + 5$

2. $4a$

3. $2a - 3$

4. $3a + 2a$

5. $5(a + 4)$

Hint: Remember to do your calculations in the correct order — use BODMAS (brackets, other, division/multiplication, addition/subtraction).

For questions 6 - 10, circle the answer in each row that is equal to the first expression.

6. $a + a$ $2(a + 1)$ $2a$ a^2

7. $3 \times \triangle - 2$ $3\triangle - 2$ $3\triangle - 6$ $3\triangle - 32$

8. $5x + 2x$ $x + 7$ $4x + 3x$ $5(x + 2)$

9. $3(2a + b)$ $6a + 6b$ $6a + 3b$ $32a + 3b$

10. $2\star - 2\star$ $2\star - 1$ $-2\star$ $2\star - 2(\star + 0)$

11. $4 \times 7 > 3x$

What is the biggest whole number that x could represent?

/11

Shine o' Grime, Wishy Washy, The Sud Buds and Top Mopz are four cleaning companies. They all charge different prices depending on the number of rooms, r, and the number of floors, f, in the house. The table gives their prices in pounds.

12. Lizzy has a house with 12 rooms and 3 floors.
Circle the company that is the cheapest for Lizzy.

     A Shine o' Grime
     B Wishy Washy
     C The Sud Buds
     D Top Mopz

Cleaning Company Prices (£)	
Shine o' Grime	$50 + r + f$
Wishy Washy	$5r + 6f$
The Sud Buds	$2rf$
Top Mopz	$30 + rf$

13. Claire has a one-floor house with 9 rooms. How much will it cost her if she hires Top Mopz to clean her house?   £

14. Rosemary uses Wishy Washy to clean her two-storey house. She spends £92. How many rooms are in her house?

15. How much money could Rosemary have saved if she had hired The Sud Buds instead?   £

/4

Algebra

16. Hiring a car costs £75 plus £50 for each day it is hired. The total cost of hiring a car, in pounds, for d days can be calculated using the expression:

$$75 + 50d$$

What is the cost of hiring a car for 9 days?   £

17. The cost of taking a coach on a ferry is £260 for the vehicle and driver, and a further £5 for each passenger. Circle the expression you could use to show the cost, in pounds, of taking a coach and n passengers on the ferry.

   A $260 - 5n$ **B** $260n - 5$ **C** $260 \times n$ **D** $260 \div 5n$ **E** $260 + 5n$

18. Paul is doing a sponsored silence. Paul works out that if he is silent for m minutes, the amount of pounds raised will be:

$$15 + 2(m + 2)$$

How many pounds will Paul raise if he is silent for 25 minutes?   £

19. Mr Lee buys a games console for £150, and some games to play on it for £35 each. If he buys n games, which expression represents the total amount he spends?

   A $150 + 35n$ **B** $150n \times 35$ **C** $150 - 35n$ **D** $150 \times 35n$ **E** $150 \times 35 \div n$

20. The time, in minutes, required to bake a cake is given by the formula $60 + 5\text{☺}$. The symbol ☺ represents the number of eggs used in the recipe. How many minutes would it take to bake a cake made with 8 eggs?   minutes

/ 5

Mr Carpenter has a 400 cm long plank of wood. He cuts off three pieces which are each x cm long.

21. Circle the expression that gives the length of wood he has left in cm.

   A $400 \div 3x$ **B** $400 - x$ **C** $400 - 3x$ **D** $400 \times 3x$ **E** $400 + 3x$

22. If $x = 90$ cm, what is the length of the plank of wood he has left?

   cm

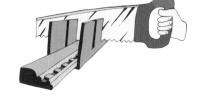

Mr Carpenter has another plank of wood which is 150 cm long. He uses all of the wood to make four shelves. He makes two shelves of length a cm, one shelf of length b cm and one shelf of length c cm. There is no wood left over.

23. Circle the equation that gives the length of the 150 cm plank of wood in terms of a, b and c.

   A $150 = 2a + b + c$ **B** $150 = a + 2b + 2c$ **C** $150 = 2(a + b + c)$ **D** $150 = a \times b \times c$

24. If $b = 30$ and $c = a + 21$, calculate a and c.

   $a =$  $c =$

/ 4

Number Sequences

Work out the missing value in each sequence.

1. 9   12   15   18   **?**

2. 113   110   107   104   **?**

3. 26   21   **?**   11   6

4. 1.25   1.5   1.75   **?**   2.25

5. **?**   8   16   32   64

Write down the fifth number in the sequence which follows each rule below.

6.   First number 6, count on in steps of 4.

7.   First number 30, count back in steps of 5.

8.   First number 3, double the previous number.

9.   First number 23, count back in steps of 3.

10. First number 5, count on in steps of 0.5.

/ 10

Peter makes up a rule for the *n*th term of a sequence.
He uses it to generate the sequence:

> 3, 7, 11, 15, 19...

Hint: n is the position of a number in a sequence. So for the 3rd term, n = 3.

11. Circle the rule below that Peter used.
     A $n + 4$ **B** $3n + 4$ **C** $4n + 3$ **D** $4n - 1$ **E** $n + 2$

12. Which of the following statements is true of any term in Peter's sequence?
     Circle the correct answer.
     A Terms can be either odd or even
     B All terms will be odd
     C All terms will be even

Peter creates a new sequence where the *n*th term is $(\frac{n}{4} + n)$.

13. Using this rule, find the two missing numbers in the sequence below.

     1.25      5

14. What is the 20th term in Peter's new sequence?

15. What term in the sequence has the value of 50? Circle the correct answer.
     A 50   **B** 45   **C** 30   **D** 40   **E** 20

/ 5

Number Sequences

Write down the total number of sticks needed to make the next shape in each of these sequences.

16.

17.

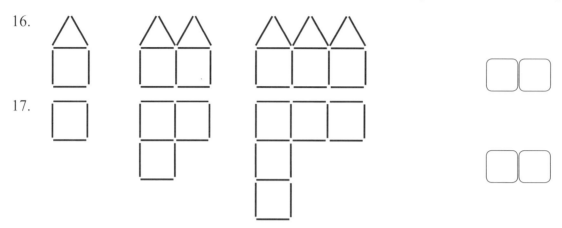

18. John writes a sequence of numbers with the rule:
    Find the difference between the two previous numbers.
    The first five numbers of his sequence are:

    20   25   5   20   15

    What is the seventh number in the sequence?

19. Tom counts back from 73 in steps of 9. Mark counts forward
    from 25 in steps of 4. What number will both boys count?

20. Nadiah counts back from 6 in steps of 1.25.
    What is the first negative number she will count?

    $-\boxed{}.\boxed{}\boxed{}$

21. Bria creates a sequence with the following rule.
    Multiply the previous number by 3 and then add 1.
    Use this rule to complete the 3rd, 4th and 5th terms in the sequence.

    2   7

/ 6

Fatima lays her marbles out in a series of patterns.

22. There are $\frac{1}{2}\,n(n + 1)$ marbles in the *n*th pattern.
    How many marbles would Fatima
    need to make the 8th pattern?

    Pattern 1   Pattern 2   Pattern 3   Pattern 4

23. Fatima rearranges her marbles
    into the following shapes.
    What is the highest shape number
    she can make with 15 marbles?

    Shape 1   Shape 2   Shape 3   Shape 4

/ 2

Section Three — Number Problems

Word Problems

1. Matt worked for 3 hours on Monday, 4 hours on Tuesday and 3 hours on Wednesday. He was paid £8 an hour. How much money did he receive?

    £ ☐ ☐ ☐

2. Two identical shirts and one tie cost £24. One shirt cost £11. What is the cost of the tie?

    £ ☐ ☐

3. Finlay got a box of 56 chocolates for his birthday. He decided to eat eight each day. After how many days had he eaten over half of the chocolates?

    ☐ ☐

4. Oscar shares out his sweets equally between his friends. They each end up with 9 sweets. Circle the amount of sweets Oscar could have started with.

    84   96   78   67   81   73   91   62   53   89

5. It takes exactly 5 litres of paint to mark out 130 parking spaces. How many parking spaces can be marked out using 3 litres of paint?

    ☐ ☐ ☐

6. Which of the following sets of items would cost exactly £6.25? Circle the correct answer.

    A   1 calculator, 1 rubber, 2 pencils
    B   4 pencils, 2 sharpeners
    C   1 calculator, 1 ruler, 1 rubber
    D   3 rulers, 3 pencils, 1 rubber
    E   1 calculator, 1 sharpener

Stationery Prices	
Calculator	£4.50
Ruler	£1.00
Pencil	25p
Rubber	75p
Sharpener	£1.50

7. Mrs Leith has five identical balls of wool weighing 750 g in total. She uses two of them to knit some mittens. What weight of wool does she have left?

    ☐ ☐ ☐ g

8. Basil is making fish pie to feed 4 people. The recipe is for 6 people, and uses 1.2 kg of fish. How many kilograms of fish should Basil buy?

    ☐ ☐ . ☐ kg

    / 8

Jack's mum goes to a sports shop to buy football kit. The prices shown are the normal retail prices.

9. Jack's mum bought him two football shirts, a pair of football boots and three pairs of socks. How much change did she get from £100?

    £ ☐ ☐ . ☐ ☐

Football Kit Prices	
Boots	£32
Shirts	£12.50
Shorts	£8.50
Socks	£2.25

10. In a football kit sale, Jack's mum could buy five pairs of socks for £10. What is the total saving compared to the normal price of five pairs of socks?

    £ ☐ ☐ . ☐ ☐

11. In the same sale, boots and shorts had a discount of 20%. How much would two pairs of shorts and a pair of football boots cost in the sale?

    £ ☐ ☐ . ☐ ☐

    / 3

Section Three — Number Problems

Word Problems

12. Connor bought six choc ices. He gave the shop assistant £7 and got 10p in change. How much did each choc ice cost?

£ ☐.☐☐

13. One jelly snake weighs 2¾ grams and costs 4p. Arthur spends 24p on jelly snakes. Circle the weight of jelly snakes he buys.
    A 11.25 g   **B** 66.5 g   **C** 36 g   **D** 16.5 g   **E** 25 g

14. Chris is serving tea and coffee at a concert. In the first hour he sells 57 drinks. Circle the statement that cannot be true.

    A   Chris sold more teas than coffees.
    B   Most people bought coffee.
    C   Chris sold five more teas than coffees.
    D   Chris sold twice as many coffees as teas.
    E   Ten more teas than coffees were sold.

15. Mr Churchill builds a brick wall. Each brick has a height of 15 cm. He puts a 2 cm thick layer of concrete between each row of bricks. He also puts a 2 cm thick concrete layer beneath the first row of bricks. The finished wall has 10 rows of bricks. How high is the wall?

    ☐☐☐☐ cm

16. A 2 litre bottle of blackcurrant concentrate makes enough squash to fill six 800 ml jugs. How many litres of concentrate are needed to fill 48 glasses, each holding 200 ml of squash?

    ☐☐ litres

17. Some Year 6 students organised a charity car wash day. They bought enough soap and wax to wash exactly 100 cars. It costs them 24p to wash each car. How much money would they raise (after taking off their costs) if they wash 100 cars, and charge £1.20 for each car?

    £ ☐☐☐

    / 6

Ben wants to make some rock cakes and lemon buns.

18. Eggs cost 22p each. How much will it cost to buy enough eggs to bake 36 rock cakes and 60 lemon buns?

    £ ☐☐.☐☐

Rock Cakes (makes 24)	
Flour	450 g
Eggs	2
Butter	200 g
Sugar	100 g
Raisins	300 g

Lemon Buns (makes 20)	
Flour	100 g
Eggs	2
Butter	100 g
Sugar	100 g
Lemon	1

19. The total cost for the ingredients of 24 rock cakes is £5.04. Assuming the cost per rock cake stays the same, calculate how much the ingredients for 70 rock cakes would cost.

    £ ☐☐.☐☐

20. Ben sells lemon buns at a school fete. Each bun costs 20p to make and is sold for 50p. He sells all the buns he made and makes £20.40 profit. How many lemon buns does he sell?

    ☐☐☐

    / 3

Data Tables

A school surveyed the ways that pupils travel to school. The results are shown in the table.

	Bus	Car	Walk	Other
Class A	15	8	7	4
Class B	14	12	5	6
Class C	9	17	6	2

1. How many pupils in Class A travel to school by car?

2. How many pupils in Class B walk to school?

3. In Class C, how many more pupils get to school by car than by bus?

4. In which class do the largest number of pupils catch a bus to school? Circle the correct answer.
    Class A   Class B   Class C

5. How many pupils in total get a car or bus to school?

6. In which class do the most pupils use a car to get to school? Circle the correct answer.
    Class A   Class B   Class C

7. How many pupils are in Class B?

/ 7

8. 40 children were asked their favourite colour out of red, green and blue.
    How many girls chose green?

	Red	Green	Blue
Boys	8	4	8
Girls	5		7

9. In a recent study, some children were asked how much pocket money they received. The results are shown in the table.

    How many children received £3.50 or less?

Amount of pocket money	Number of children
Less than £1	15
Between £1 and £3.50	12
More than £3.50 but less than £5	23
Between £5 and £10	18
More than £10	8

10. The table shows the number of pizzas sold in one hour by a takeaway.
    Fill in all the missing data in the table.

	Large	Small	Total
Pepperoni	6		8
Cheese and ham		7	
Total		9	24

/ 3

Displaying Data

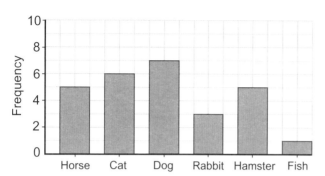

Sarah carried out a survey on her classmates. She asked them what their favourite pet was, and recorded their responses on a bar chart.

1. How many people said that rabbits were their favourite pet?

2. Which was the least popular pet? Circle the correct answer.

   A Horse   **B** Cat   **C** Dog   **D** Rabbit   **E** Hamster   **F** Fish

3. How many more people preferred cats than preferred hamsters?

4. How many more people preferred dogs than preferred fish?

5. How many people did Sarah survey in total?

6. Which two pets were equally popular? Circle both answers.

   A Horse   **B** Cat   **C** Dog   **D** Rabbit   **E** Hamster   **F** Fish

/ 6

---

7. The pictogram shows the number of fish in an aquarium.

   How many Blue Acara fish are in the aquarium?

Type of fish	Number of fish
Angelfish	
Blue Acara	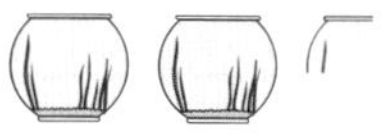
Clownfish	

= 20 fish

---

8. A cinema has 450 seats. The bar chart shows the number of people who watched the 7 pm film each evening one week.

   How many seats were empty on Friday? Circle the correct answer.

   A 75   **B** 125   **C** 25   **D** 375   **E** 50

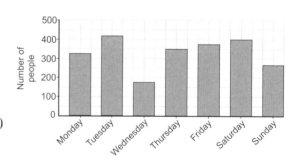

---

9. This pictogram shows the number of drinks bought at a school disco.

   How many more children bought blackcurrant than bought cherryade?

Type of drink	Number bought
Orange	
Blackcurrant	
Cherryade	

 = 4 drinks

/ 3

Displaying Data

10. A survey asked teenagers about how they spend their pocket money. The results are shown in the pie chart.

    18 teenagers said they preferred to spend their pocket money on technology. How many teenagers were interviewed altogether? Circle the correct answer.

    A 75   **B** 36   **C** 54   **D** 72   **E** 58

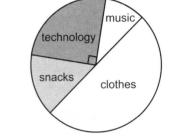

This line graph shows the distance travelled by Joe when he took his dog for a walk.

11. During his walk he stopped to talk to a friend. How long did they talk for? ☐☐ minutes

12. After how many minutes had Joe walked half of the total distance? ☐☐ minutes

This pie chart shows the proportion of tickets sold for different sports at an athletics event.

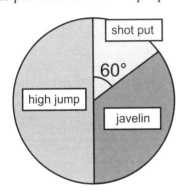

13. 250 tickets were sold for the shot put. How many tickets were sold for the high jump?

    ☐☐☐☐

14. How many tickets were sold for the javelin?

    ☐☐☐☐

/ 5

This line graph can be used to convert pounds (£) to dollars ($).

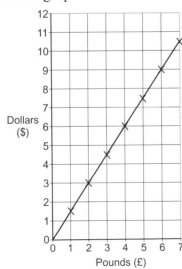

15. How many dollars is £3 worth?

    $ ☐.☐☐

16. How many pounds is $6 worth?

    £ ☐.☐☐

17. How many pounds is $45 worth?

    £ ☐☐☐.☐☐

/ 3

Section Four — Data Handling

Mean, Median, Mode and Range

What is the mode of each the following sets of numbers?

1. 6, 6, 8, 5, 10

4. 4, 6, 8, 3, 4, 10, 3, 2, 3

2. 17, 19, 18, 12, 19

5. 10, 11, 19, 18, 14, 19, 12, 19, 17

3. 14, 18, 17, 18, 15

6. 32, 40, 41, 40, 41, 32, 40

Give the median of each list of numbers below.

7. 7, 9, 12, 14, 17

10. 59, 63, 57, 21, 34, 82

8. 21, 19, 18, 11, 9

11. 23, 14, 35, 28, 32, 27

9. 5, 6, 8, 8, 9, 11

12. 13, 16, 12, 32, 9, 33

/ 12

13. Bently Rovers scored the following numbers of goals in their matches last season.

0, 2, 4, 2, 5, 1, 0, 2

What was the mean number of goals that they scored?

This table shows the daily temperatures (in °C) for Weymouth over one week.

	Monday	Tuesday	Wednesday	Thursday	Friday	Saturday	Sunday
High	14	14	10	4	6	11	9
Low	12	6	4	-3	-1	4	6

14. Circle the day that had the largest range in temperature.

Monday   Tuesday   Wednesday   Thursday   Friday   Saturday   Sunday

15. What was the mode for the high temperatures over the week?   °C

16. What was the mean of the low temperatures over the week?   °C

17. What was the median temperature for the low temperatures for the week?   °C

18. Here are the results of Phillip's last six spelling tests.

4, 6, 7, ?, 10, 5

His mean score was 7. What did he score in his fourth test?

/ 6

Section Four — Data Handling

Misleading Data

1. This is a misleading news report.

> **Landslide Victory for Popular Pupil**
>
> Yesterday, there was a landslide victory in a school election between five pupils for the next school representative. Just 12 children chose Anne, ten percent picked Hasim, 25% wanted Jamie to be their representative and 5% voted for Ted. Lex didn't get any votes.

Who became the new school representative? Circle the correct answer.

A Anne   **B** Hasim   **C** Jamie   **D** Ted   **E** Lex

2. The pictogram shows the number of animals in a zoo.

Name of Animal	Number in Zoo
Crocodile	🐊 🐊 🐊
Elephant	🐘 🐘
Snake	🐍 🐍 🐍 🐍 🐍 ◖
Monkey	🐒 🐒 🐒 ◖

1 picture = 4 animals

Why is the pictogram misleading?
Circle the letter next to the correct answer.

A It doesn't show other animals in the zoo.
B The categories are not in order.
C The pictures are not the same size.
D There cannot be half a monkey.
E Not all zoos have the same animals.

3. Which of the statements below describes why this line graph is misleading?
Circle the letter next to the correct answer.

A It is not a straight line.
B The horizontal scale is not numbered.
C The result for Thursday looks wrong.
D The vertical scale does not go up in even steps.
E Saturday and Sunday are not included.

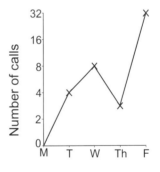

4. This misleading bar chart shows the eye colours of children in Year 6. Which of the following statements is true? Circle the letter next to the correct answer.

A The number of people with blue eyes is double the number with brown eyes.
B The number of people with hazel eyes is $\frac{2}{3}$ of the number with blue eyes.
C The number of people with green eyes is 3 times as many as those with blue eyes.
D The number of people with blue eyes is $\frac{3}{4}$ of the number with green eyes.
E The number of people with green eyes is 5 times as many as those with brown eyes.

/ 4

Section Four — Data Handling

Probability

The spinner below is divided into eight sections of equal size. Use it to answer the following questions. Write the answers to questions 1 - 3 as fractions.

1. What is the probability that the spinner will land on 4?

2. What is the probability that the spinner will land on an odd number?

3. What is the probability that the spinner will land on 7?

4. Which number is the spinner least likely to land on? Circle the correct answer.
   A 3   **B** 4   **C** 5

5. Which number has a 50% chance of being spun?

Write the answers to questions 6 - 9 as fractions in their simplest form.

6. What is the probability of throwing an even number using a dice numbered 1 to 6?

7. What is the probability of randomly choosing a red marble from a jar containing 5 red, 1 blue and 6 green marbles?

8. What is the probability of randomly choosing a green marble from a jar containing 2 red, 7 green and 3 blue marbles?

9. What is the probability of randomly choosing a striped sock from a drawer containing 2 plain, 4 spotty and 3 striped socks?

/ 9

10. Letter tiles spelling the word MATHEMATICS are placed into a bag. Frankie randomly picks a tile. What is the probability of Frankie picking a tile that is not M, S or A?

11. A box contains yellow, red and green scarves. Sandra has a $\frac{1}{4}$ chance of randomly choosing a yellow scarf. If there are 16 scarves in the box and 5 of them are green, how many are red?

12. The table shows the jams made by Mrs Jameson. She picked a jar at random. Circle the letter on the probability scale that shows the probability of the jam being strawberry.

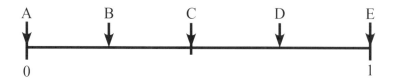

Variety	Number of jars
Apple	6
Plum	3
Strawberry	4
Raspberry	3

13. A bag of 24 sweets contains equal numbers of four different types: mice, bears, snakes and frogs. Grace offers the bag to three friends who each take a sweet at random. The first two friends both get a bear. What is the probability that the third friend will also get a bear?

/ 4

Angles

Use the diagram to answer questions 1 to 3.

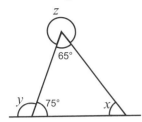

1. Calculate the size of angle x.  °

2. Calculate the size of angle y.  °

3. Calculate the size of angle z.  °

4. Angles A, B and C lie around the same point and form a straight line. What is the total of these three angles?  °

5. Angles S, T and U lie around the same point and form a straight line. If S is 34° and T is 23°, what is the size of U?  °

6. A triangle has one right angle and one angle of 67°. What is the size of the other angle?  °

7. Estimate the size of angle a. Circle the correct answer.

   A 75°   **B** 45°   **C** 15°   **D** 90°   **E** 125°

8. Which of these shapes contains at least one obtuse angle? Circle the correct answer.

9. Grace drew a shape using a square and two equilateral triangles. What is the size of the shaded angle in her shape?  °

10. The minute hand on this clock turns 300° clockwise. What number is it now pointing to?

Jimmy draws the shape below on a piece of paper.

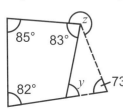

11. What is the size of angle y?  °

12. What is the size of angle z?  °

/ 12

2D Shapes

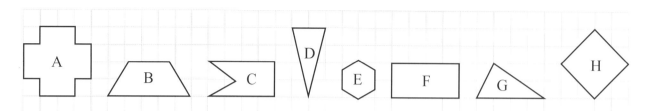

Use the shapes above to answer questions 1-5 below. Write the correct letter of the shape in the box.

1. Which shape has exactly two right angles?

2. Which shape is an isosceles triangle?

3. Which shape is a pentagon?

4. Which quadrilateral has all sides equal in length?

5. Which shape has just one pair of parallel sides and no right angles?

/ 5

6. Which one of the following shapes doesn't have two pairs of parallel sides?
    Circle the correct answer.

    A Square   **B** Rhombus   **C** Rectangle   **D** Parallelogram   **E** Trapezium

7. Which of these regular polygons has the largest internal angle? Circle the correct answer.

    A Triangle   **B** Octagon   **C** Pentagon   **D** Hexagon   **E** Square

8. Which type of triangle has a pair of perpendicular sides? Circle the correct answer.

    A Equilateral   **B** Isosceles   **C** Scalene   **D** Right-angled

/ 3

This shape is made from a square (BCDE) and an isosceles triangle (ABE).
Use the shape to answer questions 9-12 below.

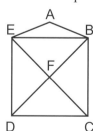

9. Which line is parallel to DE? Circle the correct answer.

    BE   BC   CE   AB   CD

10. Which line is equal in length to AE? Circle the correct answer.

    CF   BE   BF   ED   AB

11. What shape is made by joining points ABFE? Circle the correct answer.

    A Kite   **B** Square   **C** Pentagon   **D** Rhombus   **E** Trapezium

12. What shape is formed by joining points BCDEF? Circle the correct answer.

    A Kite   **B** Square   **C** Pentagon   **D** Rhombus   **E** Trapezium

/ 4

2D Shapes

13. Which of these shapes cannot be sorted into any of the cells in this table?
Circle the correct answer.

	At least one right angle	No right angles
Triangle		
Quadrilateral		

14. Joelle has drawn this kite.
What size is angle *x*?

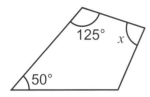

□□□ °

15. The isosceles triangle shown is reflected in the mirror line to make a four-sided shape.
What is the name of the shape that is made? Circle the correct answer.

  A Parallelogram   **C** Rhombus   **E** Square

  B Trapezium   **D** Kite

16. This traffic sign has a diameter of 900 mm.
What is the radius of the sign?

□□□□ mm

17. Mr Johnson wants to buy tiles that fit together with other identical tiles without leaving gaps between them. Which of these tiles should he not choose? Circle the correct answer.

18. This rhombus has two
angles that are both 30°.
What size is angle *a*?

□□□ °

19. Darma thinks of a shape. It is a quadrilateral with two pairs of equal sides but no parallel sides. One pair of angles is equal.
What shape is Darma thinking of? Circle the correct answer.

  A Rectangle   **B** Rhombus   **C** Trapezium   **D** Square   **E** Kite

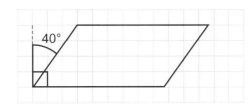

20. What size is each obtuse angle in this parallelogram?

□□□ °

/ 8

Section Five — Shape and Space

2D Shapes — Perimeter and Area

1. Which two shapes on this grid have the same area?
   Circle the correct answer.

   B and C   A and B   C and D   A and C   A and D

The dimensions of four shapes are shown.

The diagrams on this page are not drawn to scale.

2. What is the perimeter of shape S? ☐☐ cm

3. What is the perimeter of shape R? ☐☐ cm

4. What is the perimeter of shape T? ☐☐ cm

5. What is the area of shape S? ☐☐ cm²

6. What is the area of shape U? ☐☐ cm²

/ 6

7. A coffee table is in the shape of a regular pentagon. One side is 25 cm in length. What is the perimeter of the table? ☐☐☐ cm

8. A rectangular carpet has an area of 75 m². It is 15 metres long. How wide is it? ☐☐ m

9. The school playground is a regular octagon. It has a perimeter of 560 m. What is the length of each edge? ☐☐☐ m

10. The diagram shows the sheep pen being built by Farmer Brown. He wants to enclose the pen completely using 2 m wide fence panels. How many panels will he need? ☐☐

11. Julie makes this pattern using three identical kite-shaped tiles. The perimeter of the pattern is 30 cm. What is the length of side a? ☐☐ cm

12. What is the area of the shape to the left? ☐☐☐ cm²

/ 6

2D Shapes — Perimeter and Area

13. Mr Robinson built the patio on the right using hexagonal slabs. The slabs are regular hexagons with a side length of 30 cm. What is the perimeter of the patio?

☐☐☐ cm

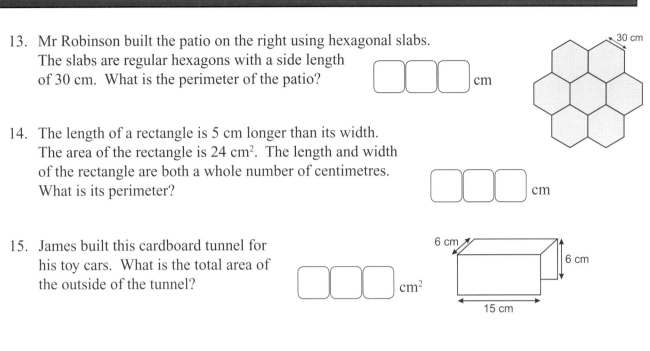
30 cm

14. The length of a rectangle is 5 cm longer than its width. The area of the rectangle is 24 cm². The length and width of the rectangle are both a whole number of centimetres. What is its perimeter?

☐☐☐ cm

15. James built this cardboard tunnel for his toy cars. What is the total area of the outside of the tunnel?

☐☐☐ cm²

6 cm
6 cm
15 cm

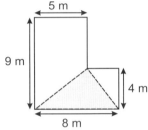
5 m
9 m
4 m
8 m

The diagram shows a plan of Geoff's garden. In heavy rainfall the shaded area of the garden floods.

16. Calculate the area of Geoff's garden.

 m²

17. Calculate the area of Geoff's garden that floods.

 m²

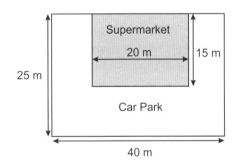
Supermarket
20 m
15 m
25 m
Car Park
40 m

18. The diagram shows a plan of a supermarket and car park. What is the area of the car park?

 m²

Each brick in this wall is 5 cm tall and 10 cm long.

5 cm
10 cm

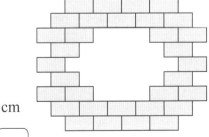

Each brick is exactly centred over the two that it rests on.

19. What is the perimeter of the hole in the wall?  cm

20. What is the area of the hole in the wall? ☐☐☐☐ cm²

21. Martha is painting four walls in her house. Each wall is 4 m wide and 2 m tall. If each tin of paint contains enough paint for 12 m² of wall, how many tins will Martha need?

/9

Section Five — Shape and Space

Symmetry

Look carefully at this set of letters and use them to answer questions 1 to 4 below.

W R D H F N

1. Which letter has two lines of symmetry?

2. Which letter only has a vertical line of symmetry?

3. Which letter only has a horizontal line of symmetry?

4. How many of the letters have no lines of symmetry? Circle the correct answer.

      1   2   3   4   5   6

5. Which of these triangles has a horizontal line of symmetry? Circle the correct answer.

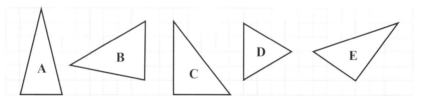

6. Which of these shapes has rotational symmetry?
   Circle the letter underneath the correct answer.

   A   **B**   **C**   **D**   **E**

Hint: A shape has rotational symmetry if it fits onto itself more than once when it is rotated about its centre.

7. Harish reflects the parallelogram on the right in the mirror line to make a new shape.
   What is the shape that Harish makes? Circle the correct answer.

   A Triangle   **B** Quadrilateral   **C** Pentagon   **D** Hexagon   **E** Heptagon

Tariq shades squares on a grid to make the following patterns.

      A   B   C   D   E

8. Which pattern has a diagonal line of symmetry?

9. Which pattern has rotational symmetry of order two,
   but no lines of reflection?

10. Tariq shades two more squares on one of the patterns and increases
    the order of rotational symmetry. Which pattern does he change?

    / 10

Section Five — Shape and Space

3D Shapes

Use these 3D shapes to answer questions 1-5 below.

   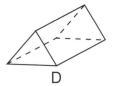

A   B   C   D   E

1. How many rectangular faces does shape A have?

2. Which shape has six identical faces?

3. Which shape has five faces and nine edges?

4. Which shape has fewer edges than faces?

5. Which shape has five faces, eight edges and five vertices?

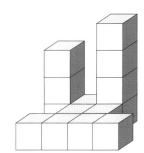

6. Ruth built this shape using 1 cm cubes. What is the volume of this shape?

   cm³

7. What is the largest number of 1 cm cubes that will fit into this box?

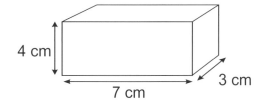

4 cm   7 cm   3 cm

8. Which of these nets will fold up to form a cube? Circle the correct answer.

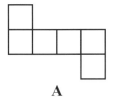   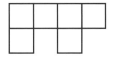   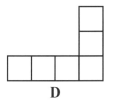   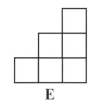

A   **B**   **C**   **D**   **E**

Prism   More than two quadrilateral faces

A   B   C   D   E

At least one curved edge

9. Elizabeth is sorting solid shapes using a Venn diagram. In which section should she place a cuboid? Circle the correct answer.

A   **B**   **C**   **D**   **E**

/ 9

3D Shapes

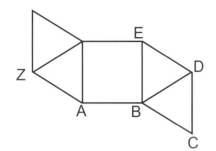

10. Karen folds this net to make a 3D shape.
    Which point joins to corner Z? Circle the correct answer.

    A   **B**   **C**   **D**   **E**

11. Katie wants to make a cube where all the opposite faces have the same letter.
    Which net must she use? Circle the correct answer.

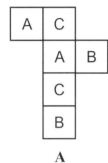 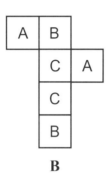 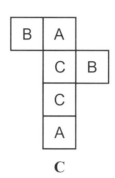 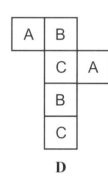 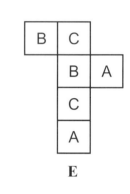

      A   **B**   **C**   **D**   **E**

12. Ravi is tidying his bedroom. How many cubes with
    edges of length 4 cm can he fit into his toy box?
    Circle the correct answer.

    A 90   **B** 180   **C** 406   **D** 30   **E** 360

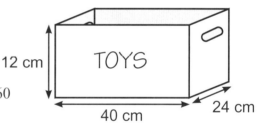

13. Each of these nets can make one of the 3D shapes A-E.
    Which 3D shape does not have a matching net? Circle the correct answer.

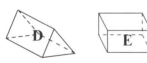 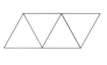

14. A house brick has a volume of 800 cm³.
    If it is 20 cm long and 5 cm high, how wide is it?  cm

15. Peter stacks a cuboid and a cube to make this shape.
    What is the total volume of the shape he has made?

     m³

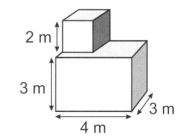

 / 6

Shape Problems

Write down the letter of the shape you would get if you did each action in questions 1 to 5 to shape X.

1. Rotate 90° clockwise.

2. Reflect in a vertical mirror line.

3. Rotate 180° anticlockwise.

4. Reflect in a horizontal mirror line.

5. Reflect in a diagonal mirror line.

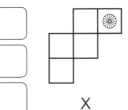 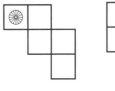

X   A   B

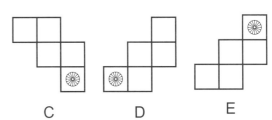

C   D   E

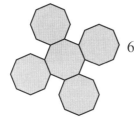

6. This shape is made up of identical regular octagons. The perimeter of the shape is 64 cm. How long is each side of the octagons?  cm

7. Jimmy built these steps using 6 wooden cubes. He glued them together and then painted the outside. He did not paint the base. How many cube faces did he paint?

    Hint: Don't forget the faces that you can't see.

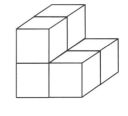

8. Marcia wants to build this model using bricks that have a length and height of 2 cm and a width of 1 cm. How many bricks does she need to make her model?

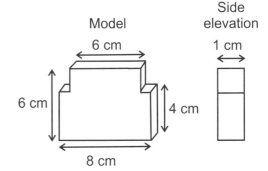

Model
Side elevation

9. Jasmine uses tiles to make this shape. Which of the options shows the outline of the shape when it has been reflected in a vertical mirror line? Circle the correct answer.

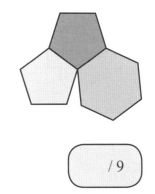

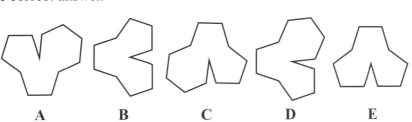

A   **B**   **C**   **D**   **E**

/9

Section Five — Shape and Space

Shape Problems

Cynthia bought a box of equilateral triangle shaped tiles, as shown.
She used the tiles to make different shapes.

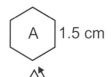

Shapes A and B show the outlines of two of the shapes she made.

10. Shape A is a regular hexagon.
    How many tiles did she use to make shape A?

11. She used 9 tiles to make shape B.
    How long is side *x*?

 cm

12. Which shape shows this tile pattern after it has been rotated 90° anticlockwise? Circle the correct answer.

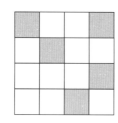

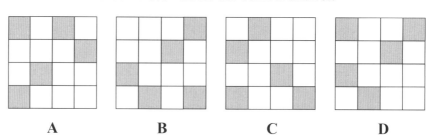

A   B   C   D

Fiona and Kim made exactly the same shape using seven cubes.
Fiona made shape Z.

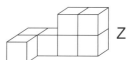

13. Which shape did Kim make? Circle the correct answer.

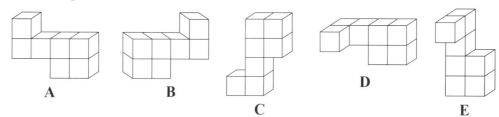

A   B   C   D   E

14. Which diagram below shows a plan view of Fiona's shape? Circle the correct answer.

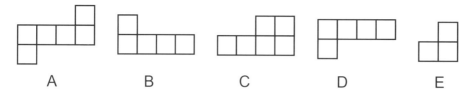

A   B   C   D   E

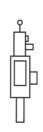

15. This is a side elevation of Claudia's robot.
    Which of the diagrams below could not be a front elevation of her robot?
    Circle the correct answer.

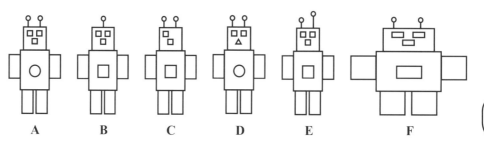

A   B   C   D   E   F

/ 6

Coordinates

The coordinate grid shows the location of attractions at a fun fair.

1. What are the coordinates of the big dipper?

2. What are the coordinates of the go-karts?

3. What are the coordinates of the carousel?

4. What are the coordinates of the ghost train?

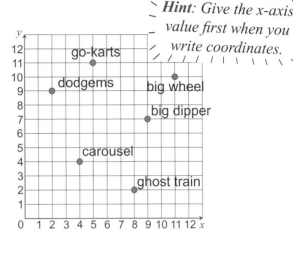

Hint: Give the x-axis value first when you write coordinates.

5. What are the coordinates of the dodgems?

6. Ted starts at point A. He moves 4 squares west and then 7 squares north. What are the coordinates of the point he finishes at?

   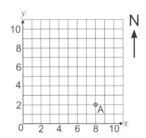

7. A line LM is drawn on the grid parallel to the line JK.

   What could the coordinates of point L be? Circle the correct answer.

   A $(-7, 0)$ **C** $(5, -2)$ **E** $(0, -1)$

   B $(-1, 0)$ **D** $(7, 0)$

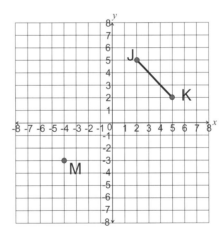

8. A square has corners positioned at $(2, 2)$, $(2, 7)$, $(7, 7)$ and $(7, 2)$.
   Which of the following points lies outside of the shape? Circle the correct answer.

   A $(3, 6)$ **B** $(5, 4)$ **C** $(8, 4)$ **D** $(2, 3)$ **E** $(7, 6)$

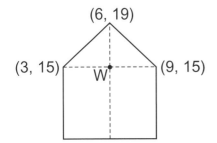

9. A pentagon is drawn on a grid. The coordinates of its corners are given. Two lines are drawn on the pentagon. What are the coordinates of their intersection, W?

/ 9

Section Five — Shape and Space

Transformations

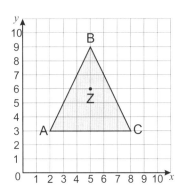

1. The triangle on the grid is rotated 90° clockwise about point Z.
What are the coordinates of the image of corner B?

2. Charlie drew a shape onto a coordinate grid.
He reflected his shape in the mirror line shown.
What are the coordinates of the image of point G?
Circle the correct answer.

   A (0, 4)   **C** (-4, 0)   **E** (-4, 4)

   B (-5, 4)   **D** (-4, 5)

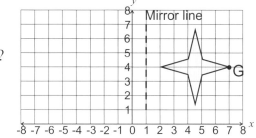

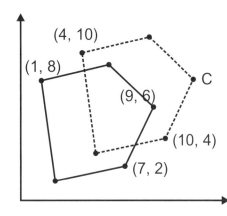

3. A pentagon is translated to a new position as shown.
What are the coordinates of point C?

4. Remi draws a square as shown. She translates the
square so that the coordinates of point X are (2, 4).
What are the coordinates of the image of point W?

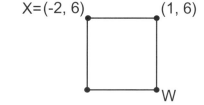

Maggie drew a cross on a grid as shown. She performed two transformations on her shape.

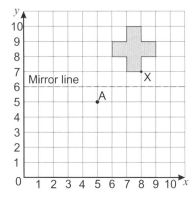

5. First, she rotated the shape 180° clockwise about point A.
What are the coordinates of the image of point X?

6. Next she reflected the new shape in the mirror line shown.
What are the coordinates of the image of point X?

/ 6

Section Five — Shape and Space

Units

Answer questions 1-4 using options **A** to **D**.
Which of these units would you choose to measure the following?

    A km   **B** cm   **C** m   **D** mm

1.   The height of a rabbit.

2.   The distance between London and Liverpool.

3.   The height of a building.

4.   The thickness of a coin.

5.   Tom bought a melon with a mass of 1.56 kilograms.
    What is the mass of the melon in grams?   g

6.   A jug holds 2.5 litres.
    How many millilitres is this?   ml

7.   Juan is 128 centimetres tall.
    How tall is he in metres?   m

8.   Tracy walked 15.3 kilometres.
    How many metres did she walk?   m

9.   A bucket contains 4500 grams of sand.
    What is the mass of the sand in kilograms?   kg

10.   Which of the following is the most likely mass of a pencil? Circle the correct answer.
     A 5.4 kg   **B** 5400 g   **C** 5.4 g   **D** 54 kg   **E** 2.54 kg

11.   Farmer Jones fills 32 bags with carrots. Each bag contains the
    same mass of carrots. The total mass of the carrots is 16 kg.
    What mass of carrots, in grams, is in each bag?   g

12.   Which container will hold about 1 litre of water? Circle the correct answer.
     A egg cup   **B** teacup   **C** dustbin   **D** small saucepan   **E** teaspoon

/ 12

13.   Look at the weighing scale on the right.
    What is the weight of this parcel in grams?   g

14.   Another parcel of the same weight is added to
    the scales. What will the reading on the scales be now?   g

15.   Parcels are sent in sacks of no more than 2 kg. What is the
    largest number of these parcels that can be sent in one sack?

/ 3

Units

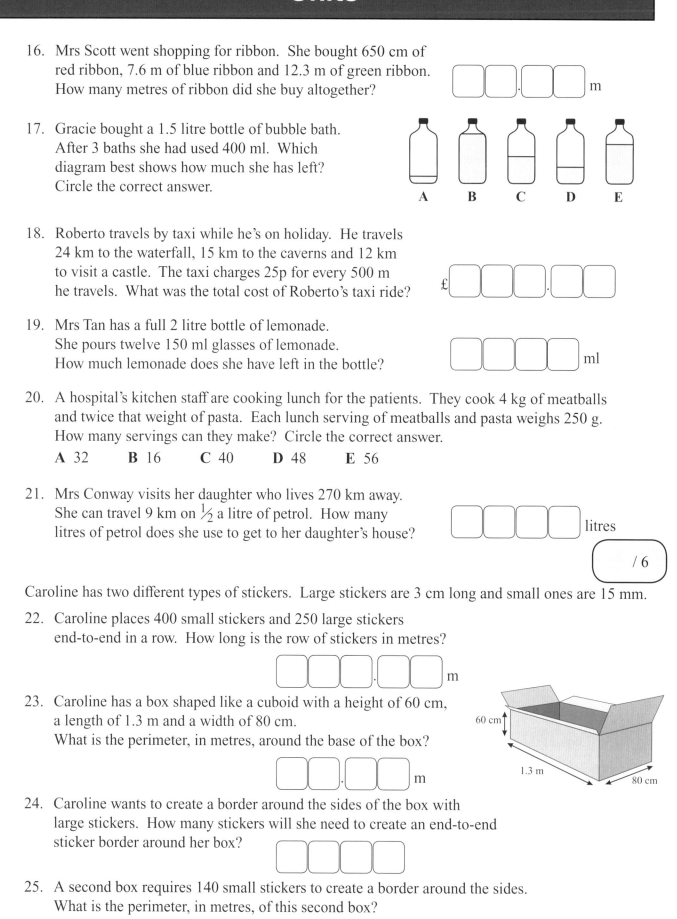

16. Mrs Scott went shopping for ribbon. She bought 650 cm of red ribbon, 7.6 m of blue ribbon and 12.3 m of green ribbon. How many metres of ribbon did she buy altogether?

☐☐.☐☐ m

17. Gracie bought a 1.5 litre bottle of bubble bath. After 3 baths she had used 400 ml. Which diagram best shows how much she has left? Circle the correct answer.

A   B   C   D   E

18. Roberto travels by taxi while he's on holiday. He travels 24 km to the waterfall, 15 km to the caverns and 12 km to visit a castle. The taxi charges 25p for every 500 m he travels. What was the total cost of Roberto's taxi ride?

£☐☐☐.☐☐

19. Mrs Tan has a full 2 litre bottle of lemonade. She pours twelve 150 ml glasses of lemonade. How much lemonade does she have left in the bottle?

☐☐☐☐ ml

20. A hospital's kitchen staff are cooking lunch for the patients. They cook 4 kg of meatballs and twice that weight of pasta. Each lunch serving of meatballs and pasta weighs 250 g. How many servings can they make? Circle the correct answer.

A 32   B 16   C 40   D 48   E 56

21. Mrs Conway visits her daughter who lives 270 km away. She can travel 9 km on ½ a litre of petrol. How many litres of petrol does she use to get to her daughter's house?

☐☐☐☐ litres

/ 6

Caroline has two different types of stickers. Large stickers are 3 cm long and small ones are 15 mm.

22. Caroline places 400 small stickers and 250 large stickers end-to-end in a row. How long is the row of stickers in metres?

☐☐☐.☐☐ m

23. Caroline has a box shaped like a cuboid with a height of 60 cm, a length of 1.3 m and a width of 80 cm. What is the perimeter, in metres, around the base of the box?

☐☐.☐☐ m

60 cm

1.3 m   80 cm

24. Caroline wants to create a border around the sides of the box with large stickers. How many stickers will she need to create an end-to-end sticker border around her box?

☐☐☐☐

25. A second box requires 140 small stickers to create a border around the sides. What is the perimeter, in metres, of this second box?

☐.☐☐ m

/ 4

Time

Use these clocks to answer questions 1-5 below.

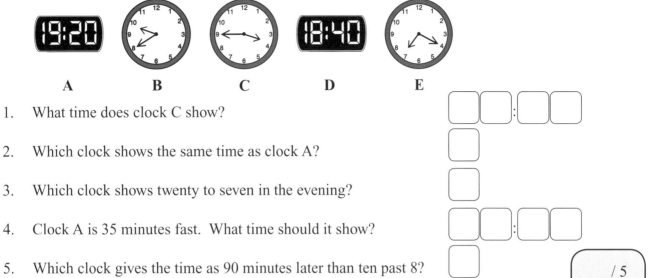

A   B   C   D   E

1. What time does clock C show?   ☐☐:☐☐

2. Which clock shows the same time as clock A?   ☐

3. Which clock shows twenty to seven in the evening?   ☐

4. Clock A is 35 minutes fast. What time should it show?   ☐☐:☐☐

5. Which clock gives the time as 90 minutes later than ten past 8?   ☐   / 5

Look at this bus timetable.

Bus number	Bus Station	High Street	Bank Street	Bigsby Road	Clayton Close	Hospital
35	10:15	10:25	10:40	10:55	11:07	11:20
42	11:25		11:45	12:00	12:12	12:37

6. How long does it take the number 35 bus
    to get from the Bus Station to Bank Street?   ☐☐ minutes

7. How long does it take the number 42 bus to
    travel from the Bus Station to Bigsby Road?   ☐☐ minutes

8. How long is the journey from Bank Street
    to Clayton Close on the number 35 bus?   ☐☐ minutes

9. How much longer does it take the
    number 42 bus to get from the Bus Station   ☐☐ minutes
    to the Hospital than the number 35 bus?

10. Which of these dates is closest to 15th August? Circle the correct answer.
    A 23rd May   **B** 19th December   **C** 4th October   **D** 28th July   **E** 10th March

11. Mary's birthday is 12 days after Alan's. Alan celebrates his birthday on the 27th September.
    Circle the date of Mary's birthday.
    A 11th October   **B** 10th November   **C** 10th October   **D** 9th October   **E** 9th November

Jo and Kat went to see a play. The play started at 10:30.

12. Kat allowed 12 minutes for the walk to the theatre and
    5 minutes to find her seat. What time did she leave?   ☐☐:☐☐

13. Jo left 16 minutes after Kat. It took her 9 minutes to walk to the
    theatre and 3 minutes to find her seat. How late was Jo for the play?   ☐☐ minutes

/ 8

Time

14. Thomas won a race with a time of $3\frac{3}{4}$ minutes.
    How many seconds is this? Circle the correct answer.
    A 225   **B** 190   **C** 300   **D** 250   **E** 45

15. All of these times are shown in the 24-hour clock.
    Circle the clock that shows 25 minutes to midnight.

    `11:35` `12:25` `23:25` `11:25` `23:35`
      A   B   C   D   E

16. Mr Smith started to paint his fence at quarter to ten in
    the morning and finished it at 5.15 pm. If he took an
    hour off for lunch, how many hours was he painting for?   ☐ hours ☐☐ minutes

17. Todd, Sam and Patrick all had swimming lessons one after the other.
    Each lesson lasted the same amount of time. Their lessons lasted
    for 2 hours and 15 minutes altogether. How long was each lesson?   ☐☐ minutes

18. If 18th May is a Tuesday, what day of the week is 18th June? Circle the correct answer.

    Monday   Tuesday   Wednesday   Thursday   Friday   Saturday   Sunday

19. Jenny spends 25 minutes on her homework each night for
    five nights each week. How long (in hours and minutes)
    would she spend doing her homework over two weeks?   ☐ hours ☐☐ minutes

20. Javier took 2 hours and 20 minutes to run a half-marathon. Which of these
    could have been his start and finish times? Circle the correct answer.

    A 10:20 and 12:00   **B** 11:50 and 13:10   **C** 11:10 and 13:45   **D** 11:35 and 13:55

21. Molly visited the zoo on Thursday 21st February.
    She arrived 40 minutes after the zoo opened and
    left $2\frac{1}{2}$ hours before it closed.
    Between what times was she there?

    ☐☐ : ☐☐ and ☐☐ : ☐☐

Barchester Zoo Opening Hours		
	April-October	November-March
Mon–Fri	9:30 – 17:30	10:30 – 15:30
Weekend	9:00 – 18:00	10:30 – 16:00

/ 8

This is Jessica's timetable for Monday. It shows when each activity starts.

9:00	9:10	10:15	10:50	11:10	12:15	13:20	14:40
register	maths	spelling	break	literacy	lunch	science	music

22. Spelling overruns by 12 minutes.
    What time does Jessica's break now start?   ☐☐ : ☐☐

23. Jessica leaves school to go to the dentist 35 minutes before the
    start of her literacy lesson and returns to school 5 minutes before
    the start of lunch. How many minutes is she away from school?   ☐☐☐ minutes

24. Jessica was away at the dentist for 10 minutes longer than the
    length of her music lesson. When will her music lesson end?   ☐☐ : ☐☐

/ 3

Section Six — Units and Measures

Mixed Problems

60 people were asked what colour car they drove. The results were recorded in a pie chart.

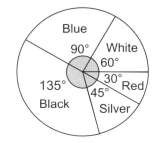

1. What percentage of people drove black or silver cars?

    %

2. Express the proportion of people who drove blue or red cars as a fraction in its simplest form.

3. Greg has a bag of peanuts. He eats $\frac{1}{20}$ of the bag each day. How many days will it take him to eat 40% of the bag of peanuts?

4. Class 6B wrote down which flavour of pie was their favourite. They showed their results in a pictogram. What is the modal favourite flavour of pie? Circle the correct answer.
   - **A** Pecan
   - **B** Rhubarb
   - **C** Pumpkin
   - **D** Blueberry

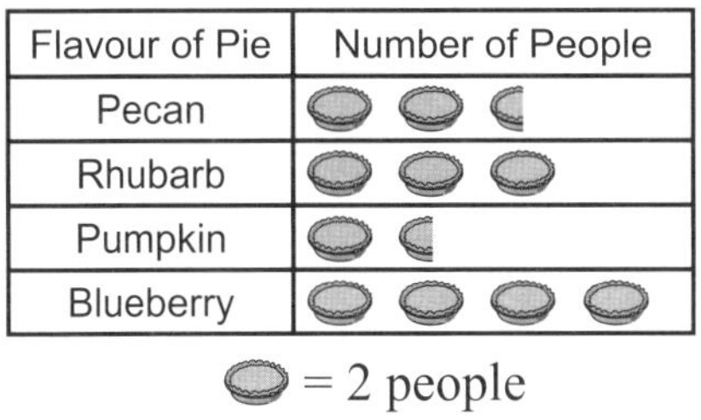

Flavour of Pie	Number of People
Pecan	🥧🥧🥮
Rhubarb	🥧🥧🥧
Pumpkin	🥧🥮
Blueberry	🥧🥧🥧🥧

🥧 = 2 people

5. Jacob buys a bag of seeds for £4.50. Each morning he puts out two cups of seeds on his bird table. The bag runs out after 9 days. How much does one cup of seeds cost?

    p

6. Miss Orchard is buying some carpet for her hallway, which is 6 m long and 150 cm wide. The carpet she has chosen costs £22 per square metre. How much will it cost to carpet her hallway in total?

   £

7. Mr Phillips filled a swimming pool with water from a hose. 20 litres of water went into the pool every minute the hose was turned on. Mr Phillips turned the hose on at 8:20 am and turned it off at 10 am. How many litres of water did he put into the pool?

    litres

8. 1 m by 4 m rolls of turf cost £80.00. Mr Taylor's yard is 5 m long and 8 m wide. How much will it cost him to turf half of his yard?

   £

9. The picture on the right shows the angle on a straight line split into 3 parts. What fraction of the total does angle x represent? Circle the correct answer.
   - **A** $\frac{1}{2}$
   - **B** $\frac{1}{4}$
   - **C** $\frac{1}{5}$
   - **D** $\frac{1}{6}$
   - **E** $\frac{1}{3}$

   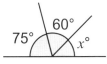

Mrs Farooq records the sizes of her gas bills on a bar chart.

10. The mean of her four bills is £80.
    How much is her bill in April?

    £

11. What is the range in the price of her gas bills from July to April?

    £

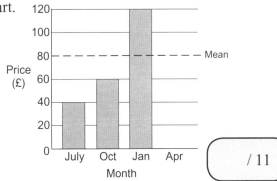

/ 11

Section Seven — Mixed Problems

Mixed Problems

12. Mr Drew weighed the crops from each of his five apple trees.
    He worked out that the mean crop weight was 320 kg. The
    crops from four of his trees were 370 kg, 280 kg, 330 kg and
    310 kg. What was the weight of the crop from the fifth tree?

 kg

13. Yussif filled this container with 1000 cm³ of water.
    What percentage of the container was filled with water?
    Circle the correct answer.

    A 30%   **B** 15%   **C** 40%   **D** 25%   **E** 20%

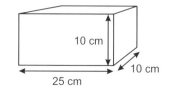

14. 40 language textbooks were put into a box.
    The number of books for each subject was
    recorded in a bar chart. Circle the probability
    of choosing a German book, at random, from the box.

    A ⅓   **B** ⅕   **C** ⅖   **D** ⅔   **E** ¼

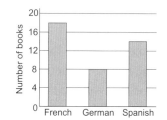

15. Lars is cleaning his windows. He has a bucket and a 600 ml bottle of washing-up liquid.
    He needs to add 5 ml of washing-up liquid to every 500 ml of water that he uses.
    If he uses 6 litres of water each time he fills his bucket, how many buckets
    could he mix before the bottle of washing-up liquid ran out?

16. Hannah has some tiles in two different shapes — squares and hexagons.
    She cuts some of the square tiles in half to make triangles
    and makes the pattern shown on the right.
    What is the area of her pattern? Circle the correct answer.   Area = S Area = H

       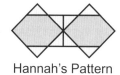
    Hannah's Pattern

    A $2H + 8S$ **B** $2H + 4S$ **C** $2H + 2S$ **D** $H + 4S$ **E** $H + 2S$

17. What is the perimeter of the shape to the right?
    Circle the correct answer.

    A $2a + 2b$ **B** $a + b$ **C** $a \times b$ **D** $2a \times 2b$ **E** $2a + b - ab$

18. Circle the rule below that gives this sequence:
          5, 12, 19, 26, 33...

    A $n + 7$ **B** $7n - 2$ **C** $7n + 2$ **D** $n + 4$ **E** $n + n^2$

19. In the same sequence, which term gives a value of 173?

20. Gerald is paid £3.50 for every half hour of work he does.
    On Saturday Gerald was at work from 6:20 am to 4:50 pm and
    he took a 1 hour unpaid lunch break. How much did he earn?   £

21. Melanie needs to take 15 ml of medicine every 2 hours. She opens a full medicine bottle
    and takes her first dose at 4 pm on Monday, and finishes the bottle of medicine with a last
    dose at 2 pm on Wednesday. How much medicine was in the bottle to start with?

 ml

/ 10

Assessment Test 1

The rest of the book contains four assessment tests to help you improve your maths skills.

Each test is divided into two parts. Section A is the 'quick maths' section — the questions here are more straightforward but with less time available per question. Section B is the 'long maths' section, the questions are more complex, but there's more time to answer them.

For each test, allow 10 minutes to do Section A and 25 minutes to do Section B. Work as quickly and as carefully as you can.

You can print **multiple-choice answer sheets** for these questions from our website — go to www.cgplearning.co.uk/11+. If you'd prefer to answer them in write-in format, either write your answers in the spaces provided or circle the **correct answer** from the options given.

Section A — Quick Maths
You have **10 minutes** to complete this section.
There are **30 questions** in this section.

---

1. Rose measures the height in cm of a plant against the ruler to the right. She marks the height with an X. How tall is the plant?

     cm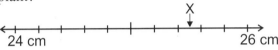

2. Kylie has a mirror which is shaped like a regular hexagon, as shown to the right. What is the size of angle *y*?

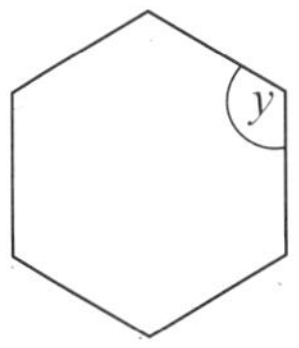

    A 180°   **B** 60°   **C** 120°   **D** 90°   **E** 175°

3. Jeff thinks of a number which can be expressed as 6 × 2 + 12. Which of the following expressions gives the same answer?

    A 48 − 8 × 3   **B** 3 + 11 × 2   **C** 3 × 7   **D** 24 ÷ 2 − 1   **E** 2 + 4 × 4

4. James saves the following notes and coins from his pocket money. How much has he saved altogether?

    £

5. Which of the following shapes could only go in the region labelled X?

    A rhombus   **D** scalene triangle
    B kite   **E** isosceles triangle
    C regular pentagon

	At least two angles equal	All angles different
At least two sides equal		
All sides different lengths		X

6. A bag of fruit costs 99p. How much will 9 bags of fruit cost?

    £

7. What is 45.952 rounded to the nearest tenth?

    A 45.9   **B** 46.0   **C** 45.95   **D** 45.96   **E** 45.10

8. Chris has a dentist appointment at ten to five in the afternoon. What is the time of his appointment on the 24-hour clock?

Carry on to the next question → →

Assessment Test 1

48

9. Bethany cuts her birthday cake into 20 equal slices. She gives out 16 slices to her friends. What fraction of the cake does Bethany have left?

   A $\frac{1}{5}$ **B** $\frac{1}{4}$ **C** $\frac{2}{5}$ **D** $\frac{1}{8}$ **E** $\frac{3}{5}$

10. Anna has a book with 1897 pages. Round the number of pages to the nearest ten.

11. An engineer charges a customer £50 for every job and £25 for every hour that he works. Which formula could you use to find how much he charges in pounds, C, for h hours of work?

    A $C = 50 \div 25h$ **B** $C = 50 + 25h$ **C** $C = 50h - 25$ **D** $C = 25 + 50h$ **E** $C = 50h$

12. 24 children want to go camping. 5 children can sleep in each tent. How many tents do they need?

13. What is the missing number in this equation?

    $2808 + 2808 + 2808 = \boxed{} \times 6$

14. The graph to the right shows how many of a particular board game have been sold each month over a 6 month period.

	Jan	Feb	Mar	Apr	May	June
Ant Alliance	50	25	10	5	20	45
Bee Bash	45	40	35	30	20	20
Croc Chase	20	10	15	25	40	40
Dodo Detective	30	35	30	35	30	30
Emu Escape	15	20	25	30	40	40

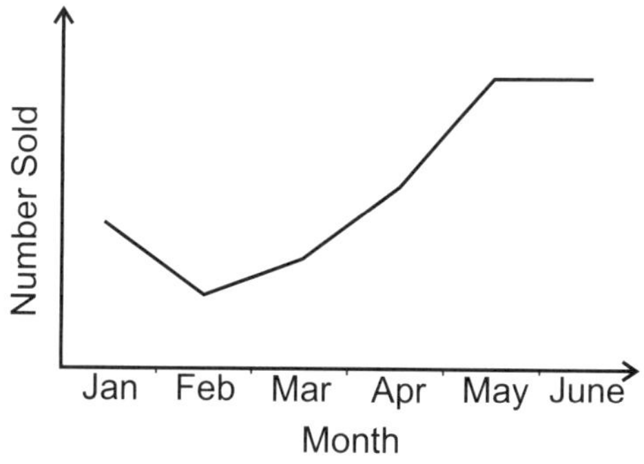

Using the information in the table, which of the games could the graph correspond to?

    A Ant Alliance   **C** Croc Chase   **E** Emu Escape
    B Bee Bash   **D** Dodo Detective

15. This pie chart shows the colours of the sun hats worn by 36 children. Find the number of children wearing yellow hats.

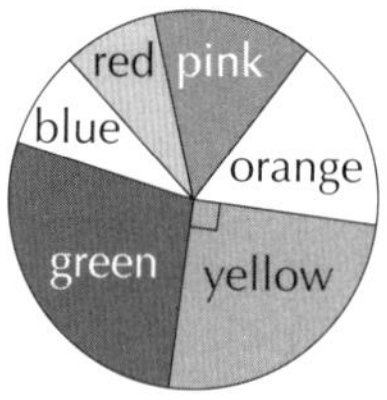

16. Johnny has a ten pound note. He spends £8.93. How much does he have left?

    £ ☐ ☐ . ☐ ☐

17. Year 5 and Year 6 are split into red, yellow and blue teams. The number of points won by each team are shown in the table. How many points did the blue team win in total?

Team	Year 5	Year 6	Total
Red	27	50	77
Yellow	32	25	57
Blue		30	
Total	90	105	

18. A packet of 6 Milky Bears normally costs 40p. They are on special offer at 10% off. What is the cost of one milky bear?

    ☐ ☐ p

Carry on to the next question → →

Assessment Test 1

19. Which of the following statements is correct?

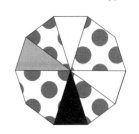

   A   The spinner is more likely to land on a grey segment than a black one.
   B   The spinner is twice as likely to land on a spotty segment as a white one.
   C   There is an even chance of the spinner landing on a spotty segment.
   D   The spinner is more likely to land on a spotty segment than any other.
   E   It is impossible for the spinner to land on a black segment.

20. Which two shapes on the right both have at least one right angle?

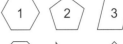

   A 1 and 2   **C** 1 and 6   **E** 2 and 4
   B 3 and 5   **D** 5 and 6

21. Laura gained the following marks in her exams.

     47   55   42   41   58   63   62   73

   Which scores are prime numbers?

   A 47, 41, 63 and 73   **C** 47, 55, 41 and 73   **E** 42, 58 and 62
   B 47, 58 and 62   **D** 47, 41 and 73

22. The rectangle on the coordinate grid is moved 3 units to the right and 2 units down. What are the new coordinates of its corners?

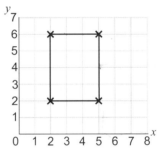

   A (3, 6), (6, 6), (6, 2), (3, 2)
   B (6, 3), (6, 6), (2, 6), (2, 3)
   C (5, 6), (8, 6), (8, 2), (5, 2)
   D (5, 4), (8, 4), (8, 0), (5, 0)
   E (4, 3), (4, 7), (7, 7), (7, 3)

23. Here are the shoe sizes of nine children at a party. What is the median shoe size?

      6 6 7 5 7 6 5

24. This honeycomb pattern is made up of regular hexagons.
The length of each side of the hexagons is 2 cm.
Calculate the distance around the outer edge of this pattern.

   cm

25. The table shows part of the information written on a tin of fruit. Amrit eats ¾ of the tin of fruit. How many grams of carbohydrate did Amrit eat?

   g

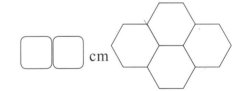

	Per ¼ tin
Protein	0.4 g
Carbohydrate	12.2 g
Fat	0.1 g
Fibre	1.2 g

26. A train timetable is shown to the right.
If Cara catches the first available train after 9:00 am from Chapel Street,
what time should she arrive in Lanston?

   :

Colwyn Gardens	08:50	09:10	09:30
Chapel Street	08:55	09:15	09:35
Bispham	09:06	09:26	09:46
Torsway	09:17	09:37	09:57
Lanston	09:45	10:05	10:25

27. Robert has two identical tiles. One is shown, marked X. He arranges the tiles on a grid. Circle the shape that cannot be made without overlapping the tiles.

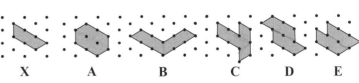

   X   **A**   **B**   **C**   **D**   **E**

Carry on to the next question →→

Assessment Test 1

28. A shop sells a different pie and a different dessert each weekday.
Dan only likes meat pies. He hates apple desserts.
Dan visits the shop on a random weekday. Circle the
probability that he will like both the pie and dessert on offer.

	Pie	Dessert
Monday	beef	lemon cake
Tuesday	mushroom	apple crumble
Wednesday	chicken	apple pie
Thursday	cheese	trifle
Friday	lamb	carrot cake

   A $\frac{2}{5}$ **B** $\frac{3}{5}$ **C** $\frac{5}{2}$ **D** $\frac{1}{2}$ **E** $\frac{5}{3}$

29. On Tuesday the temperature is 1 °C. By Wednesday it has dropped
to –2 °C. The temperature drops by twice as much from
Wednesday to Thursday. What is the temperature on Thursday?

   – ☐ ☐ °C

30. Tara uses this net to make a 3D shape.
Which corner will touch the corner marked X
when the net is folded?

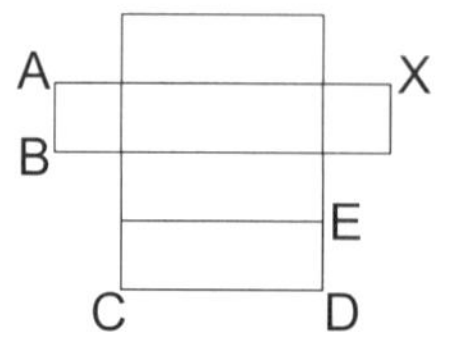

   A   **B**   **C**   **D**   **E**

   / 30

Section B — Long Maths

You have **25 minutes** to complete this section.
There are **30 questions** in this section.

Joel is shopping for fruit at a greengrocers.

1. Joel weighs a basket containing 7 peaches, as
shown on the right. Each peach weighs 200 g.
How many kilograms does the basket weigh?

   ☐ ☐ . ☐ ☐ kg

2. Joel exchanges three of the peaches for three apples.
Each apple weighs ¾ the weight of one peach.
What is the new weight of the basket and its contents?

   ☐ ☐ . ☐ ☐ kg

2.300 kg

Roger and Andy take part in a long jump competition. They have six jumps each.
They record all their jumps in metres in the table below.

	1	2	3	4	5	6
Roger	5.30	4.75	4.75	5.10	5.05	4.70
Andy	5.25	5.00	4.90	4.95	4.80	5.10

3. What is the range of the distances of Andy's jumps?   ☐ ☐ . ☐ m

4. What is the modal distance for Roger's jumps?   ☐ ☐ . ☐ m

5. What is Andy's mean distance?   ☐ ☐ . ☐ m

6. What is Roger's median jump?   ☐ ☐ . ☐ m

7. Adam thinks of a number. He multiplies it by 8, adds 6 and then divides
by 2. He ends up with 131. What was the number he started with?

   ☐ ☐ ☐ . ☐

8. A tap is dripping water at a rate of 20 ml per minute.
How long will it take for 1 litre of water to drip from the tap?

   ☐ ☐ minutes

Carry on to the next question →→

9. Jane works for a shoe shop and is given a discount card. Jane uses her card to buy a pair of trainers for £24.75. The trainers originally cost £27.50. What percentage discount does she receive?

☐☐ %

Jamie has a collection of the following shapes.

10. What is the ratio of circles to squares? Express the ratio in its simplest form.

☐ : ☐

11. What is the ratio of grey squares to white squares? Express the ratio in its simplest form.

☐ : ☐

12. Jamie chooses a shape at random. What is the probability that it will be a white circle?

A ¾   **B** ⅘   **C** ¼   **D** ½   **E** ⅕

Eve is baking cupcakes using the ingredients on the right.

13. Eve needs to make exactly 40 cakes. How much butter, in grams, will she need?

☐☐☐☐ g

14. Eve has 1.4 kg of flour. If she uses all of the flour, and assuming she has enough of the other ingredients, what is the largest number of cupcakes she could make?

☐☐☐

> **Cupcakes — makes 12**
> 240 g flour
> 3 eggs
> 150 g butter
> 150 g sugar

Each child in Ella's year group was asked to pick their favourite fruit. The results were collected in a bar chart.

15. How many more children chose plum than chose pear?

☐☐

16. Which fruit is half as popular as pear and apple combined?

A Orange   **B** Peach   **C** Plum   **D** Banana

Number of Children

17. A shop has an offer on greetings cards. You can buy 3 boxes of 20 cards for the price of 2 boxes. A box costs £3.90. Bella buys 6 boxes in the offer. She also buys a box of 12 envelopes for £1.80. How much does she spend in total?

£ ☐☐.☐☐

Kaye follows a route from point A on the grid.

18. She walks 1 square north then 2 squares east. What are the coordinates of the point her route takes her to?

(☐ , ☐)

19. From her new position, Kaye walks 2 squares south and three squares west. What are the coordinates of the point her route takes her to?

(☐ , ☐)

Carry on to the next question → →

Assessment Test 1

20. Amanda has some pocket money. She spends 60% of it
    and is left with £6.00. How much money did she start off with?
    £

21. Kate starts out on a 135 km journey at 8:50 am. She travels
    on average at 60 km per hour. What time does she arrive at
    her destination? Write your answer using the 24-hour clock.

22. A number is written on each face of the triangular-based pyramid shown on the right.
    The mean of the numbers is 4. Which of these could be the two hidden numbers?

    A 2 and 4   **B** 1 and 2   **C** 2 and 5   **D** 1 and 5   **E** 1 and 4

23. Toby has 4.4 litres of lemonade, 900 millilitres of lime juice and
    2.8 litres of orange juice. He mixes them together in a bucket.
    How many litres of liquid is in the bucket?
     litres

24. Juliet is converting her exam results into percentages from fractions.
    She scored $^{17}/_{20}$ in her English test. What is this as a percentage?
     %

25. Use the formula below to find the size of angle m if $n = 46°$.

    $m = (180 - n) \div 2$

    $m =$ 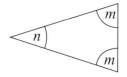 °

The playground at Jay's school is made up of six identical right-angled triangles.

26. What is the area of the playground?
     m²

    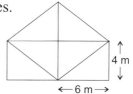

27. What is the sum of the number of lines of symmetry and
    the order of rotational symmetry of Jay's playground?

28. Jay's school are building this climbing frame
    on the playground. The frame is built of a
    wooden cube on top of a cuboid.
    What is the total volume of the frame?
     m³

    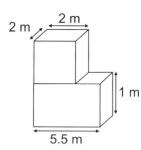

Bobby's school have been collecting 2p coins for charity. They count the coins into £1 piles.

29. Bobby decides to check the £1 piles are correct by weighing them.
    Each coin weighs 7.5 g. How many grams should each pile weigh?
     g

30. Bobby's school aim to raise £200. If they achieve their target, how
    much will it weigh in total, in kg, if all money raised is in 2p coins?
     kg

/ 30

Assessment Test 2

Allow 10 minutes to do Section A and 25 minutes to do Section B.
Work as quickly and as carefully as you can.

You can print **multiple-choice answer sheets** for these questions from our website — go to
www.cgplearning.co.uk/11+. If you'd prefer to answer them in write-in format, either write
your answers in the spaces provided or circle the **correct answer** from the options given.

Section A — Quick Maths
You have **10 minutes** to complete this section.
There are **30 questions** in this section.

1. This circle has been split into equal parts. What fraction has been shaded?

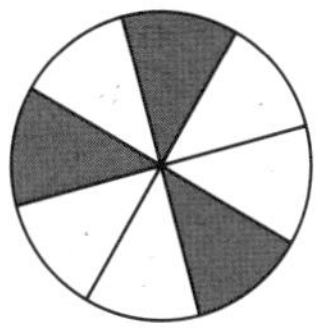

    A $\frac{5}{8}$ **B** $\frac{1}{3}$ **C** $\frac{6}{9}$ **D** $\frac{3}{8}$ **E** $\frac{5}{18}$

2. Bill goes to a car rally. He keeps a note of the race times of the cars in minutes:

    122, 133, 142, 154, 122, 156, 134

    What is the range of the times?

     minutes

3. Tahsin is doing this shape puzzle. Which of the pieces
    below will complete the puzzle?

    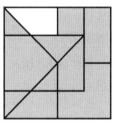

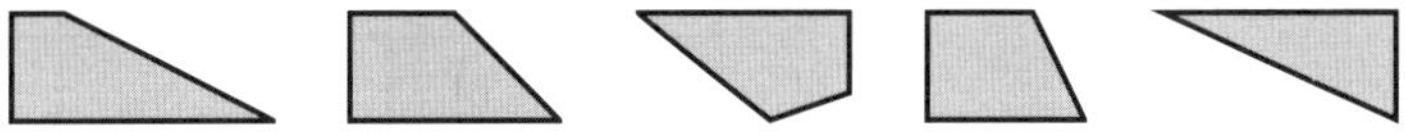

    A   **B**   **C**   **D**   **E**

4. Which of the following is most likely to be the weight of a small can of baked beans?

    A 250 g   **B** 2.5 kg   **C** 2.5 g   **D** 2500 g   **E** 25 g

5. Which of these numbers is 21^2?

    A 42   **B** 441   **C** 4410   **D** 4200   **E** 44110

6. Which of these dials shows 750 g?

    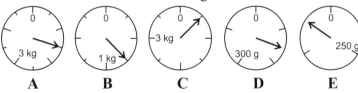

    A   **B**   **C**   **D**   **E**

7. A scarf is 45 cm long. Jade buys 20 scarves.
    What is the total length of the scarves in metres?

         m

8. Henry is 145.6 cm tall. Paul is 145.9 cm tall. Alfie is exactly halfway
    between the heights of Henry and Paul. How tall is Alfie?

         cm

Carry on to the next question →→

9. Sarinder asked her classmates what their favourite pet was.
She recorded her results in the pictogram.
How many more people liked dogs than fish?

Cat	
Dog	
Fish	
Mouse	

= 4 people

10. Elsa has a bag of sweets containing 7 chocolates, 8 toffees and 3 liquorice laces.
She takes out 2 sweets at random and eats them. They are both chocolate.
What is the probability of her randomly picking a toffee next time?

A ¼   **B** ½   **C** ⅓   **D** ⅜   **E** ⁴⁄₉

11. Ben reflects the triangle shown on this graph in the *y*-axis.
What are the coordinates of the reflection of point A?

A (3, 2)   **C** (1, 4)   **E** (2, 2)
B (−2, −2)   **D** (3, 0)

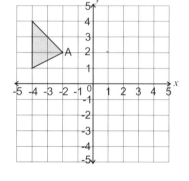

12. Eloise, Lucinda and Jennifer are given £150 by their aunt.
They are told to share it in a 5:3:2 ratio.
How much money will Lucinda receive?   £ ☐☐.☐☐

13. Where does the number 26 belong in this sorting table?

A top left-hand box   **D** bottom right-hand box
B bottom left-hand box   **E** none of these
C top right-hand box

	Even numbers	Odd numbers
Multiples of 3		
Multiples of 7		

14. David has a shaded pentagon and a clear pentagon. He places the clear pentagon on top of the shaded one and then rotates it by 180°. Which of these shapes could be the shape David makes?

A   **B**   **C**   **D**   **E**

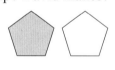

15. Mrs Burton often catches the bus from Oxton to Brixal.
Sometimes she takes Bus A, and sometimes she takes Bus B.
How long does the longest bus ride take?   ☐☐☐ minutes

	Bus A	Bus B
Oxton	09:44	11:39
Lymson	09:52	11:45
Barraw	10:31	12:16
Brixal	10:56	12:48

16. Which of these calculations will give an odd number as the answer?

A 113 × 115   **B** 142 × 623   **C** 436 × 812   **D** 147 + 189   **E** 672 + 998

17. Ten children in Class 6 were asked to give their favourite colour. The results are written in this list:

red, blue, green, silver, purple, red, gold, gold, green, red

What is the modal colour?

A Red   **B** Blue   **C** Green   **D** Silver   **E** Purple   **F** Gold

Carry on to the next question → →

18. The table shows the number of prizes won by Ester at Bingo in a week. Ester won 32 prizes altogether. How many prizes did she win on Thursday? ☐☐

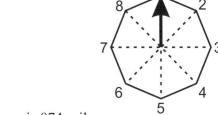

Day	Number of prizes
Monday	5
Tuesday	8
Wednesday	4
Thursday	
Friday	6

19. Which of the following statements is true?

   A $\frac{7}{100} > \frac{3}{4}$ **B** $\frac{7}{100} > 0.65$ **C** $\frac{7}{100} > 0.09$ **D** $0.65 < \frac{3}{4}$ **E** $0.65 < 0.09$

20. Lemone is opening up a plant stall in the market. She buys the stall for £S and boxes of cactus plants for £C each. Each box contains 12 cactus plants and Lemone buys 60 cactus plants altogether. Which expression shows the total cost in pounds?

   A $12SC$ **B** $S + 5C$ **C** $SC + 12$ **D** $5SC$ **E** $S + 60C$

21. The arrow on the spinner is pointing at number 1. Charlotte spins the arrow round 315° anti-clockwise. Which number is the arrow pointing at now? ☐

22. Bernard is running from Land's End to John O'Groats. The distance is 874 miles. If he runs 25 miles a day, how many days will it take him to run the distance?

   A 36   **B** 27   **C** 32   **D** 35   **E** 26

23. The diagram shows a rectangular flag. It is split into four equal rectangles. What is the area of the shaded rectangle? ☐☐ cm²

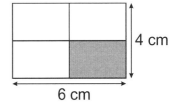

6 cm
4 cm

24. Hannah has 23 bags of sweets which each contain 14 individual sweets. She has 322 sweets in total. Jake has 46 bags of sweets. Each bag contains 140 individual sweets. How many individual sweets does Jake have in total?

   A 1288   **B** 3220   **C** 64400   **D** 6440   **E** 12888

25. Penny has a drawer containing 36 socks. She picks out one sock at random. The probability that she will pick out a white sock is $\frac{2}{3}$. How many white socks are in the drawer? ☐☐

26. Which expression gives the nth term of this sequence?
   $$-1, -1, -1, -1, -1$$
   A $2n - 3$ **B** $n - 1$ **C** $n^2 - n$ **D** $n - (n + 1)$ **E** $(n - 1)^2$

27. Julie divides a bag of 70 carrots between some rabbits. Each rabbit has exactly the same number of carrots. Julie doesn't have any carrots leftover and doesn't divide any whole carrots. How many rabbits is it possible for Julie to have fed?

   A 3   **B** 4   **C** 5   **D** 6   **E** 8

Carry on to the next question →→

Assessment Test 2

28. The grid shows a small island. Adam goes for a walk starting at (−1, −2). He travels four squares north and two squares east. What are the coordinates of the point that he reaches?

    A   (−3, 2)   B   (−2, 2)   C   (0, 3)   D   (1, 2)   E   (1, 3)

29. Jemima wants to plant a number of plants, *p,* and a number of trees, *t.* The area she needs can be written as $3p + 18t$. Which expression below is equivalent to Jemima's expression?

    A   3(6*pt*)   B   6($p + 3t$)   C $21p − 3t$ D   3($p + 6t$)   E $2p + p + 3t^2$

30. 50 people were asked what colour their car was. 16 people said blue. What percentage of people did not say blue?

    ☐☐ %

    ⬭ / 30

Section B — Long Maths

You have **25 minutes** to complete this section.
There are **30 questions** in this section.

The price of board games in a shop is shown in the table.

1. Jack gives the shopkeeper £30.00 and gets 50p change. Which games could he have bought?

Blocks	Trivia Time	Clueless	Scramble	Brainium
£12.50	£10.50	£6.50	£11.50	£9.50

    A   Scramble, Blocks and Trivia Time   D   Scramble, Blocks and Clueless
    B   Clueless, Brainium and Trivia Time   E   Scramble, Clueless and Trivia Time
    C   Blocks, Clueless and Trivia Time

2. Jill buys 2 copies of Brainium and 3 copies of Trivia Time. She pays with 3 £20 notes. How much change will Jill receive?

    £☐☐.☐☐

3. Lucy has some paper circles and some paper squares which she uses to make a rocket. The squares have sides of 4 cm and the circles have areas of 10 cm². She cuts some of the shapes in half. What is the area of her rocket?

    ☐☐ cm²

Moses is tiling his rectangular bathroom floor.

4. Each tile is 0.04 m² and he uses 100 whole tiles to cover the entire floor. If the width of his bathroom is 1 m, what is the length of his bathroom?

    ☐☐☐ m

5. Moses plans on using 2 different types of tiles on his bathroom floor. 55% of the tiles will be white and 45% will be black. Write the ratio of white to black tiles in its simplest form.

    ☐☐ : ☐☐

6. What is the total area of the bathroom floor that will be covered with black tiles?

    ☐☐.☐ m²

Carry on to the next question → →

7. Fiona arranges 6 equilateral triangles to make the shape shown. What is the size of the shaded angle?

Lisa, Amy and Louise all collect handbags.

8. Lisa has *H* handbags, Amy has *H* + 2 handbags and Louise has 2*H* handbags. Altogether, Lisa, Amy and Louise have 26 handbags. How many handbags does Louise have?

9. Georgina has three times as many handbags as Amy. Which expression correctly expresses the number of handbags Georgina has?

   A $3H + 2$ **B** $3H$ **C** $3H + 6$ **D** $3H + 3$ **E** $3(H + 6)$

10. Duncan has £2.73. He has the same number of 2p and 1p coins, and these are the only coins that he has. How many 1p coins does he have?

11. 40 girls and boys played in a football tournament. The number of goals scored and saves made during the tournament were recorded in the table. How many saves were made in total?

	Girls	Boys	Total
Goals		4	
Saves	14		
Total	24		44

Bill is filling a large packing box with small match boxes. The packing box measures 50 cm × 50 cm × 20 cm. The matchboxes measure 5 cm × 2 cm × 1 cm.

12. How many matchboxes can he fit in the packing box?

13. Each match box contains 25 matches in total. How many matches are in the packing box if it has been completely filled with match boxes?

14. Raj is buying 2 family tickets for a concert. How much does he spend?

£ ☐ ☐ . ☐ ☐

> **Concert Tickets**
> Adults   £3.50
> Children   £1.50
> 20% discount for family ticket
> (2 adults and 2 children)

Sherrie is hosting a party for 24 children and 7 adults.

15. Sherrie buys 3 sausage rolls for each child and 5 sausage rolls for each adult. If the sausage rolls come in packets of 25, how many packets will Sherrie need to buy?

16. Sherrie wants to make some cakes for the party. She needs enough for each adult to have $\frac{1}{7}$ of a cake and each child to have $\frac{1}{8}$ of a cake. How many cakes will she need to bake?

17. A plant grows 0.025 m every 6 months. It is 1.5 m tall. How many years will it take to reach 2 m?

☐ ☐ years

Carry on to the next question → →

Assessment Test 2

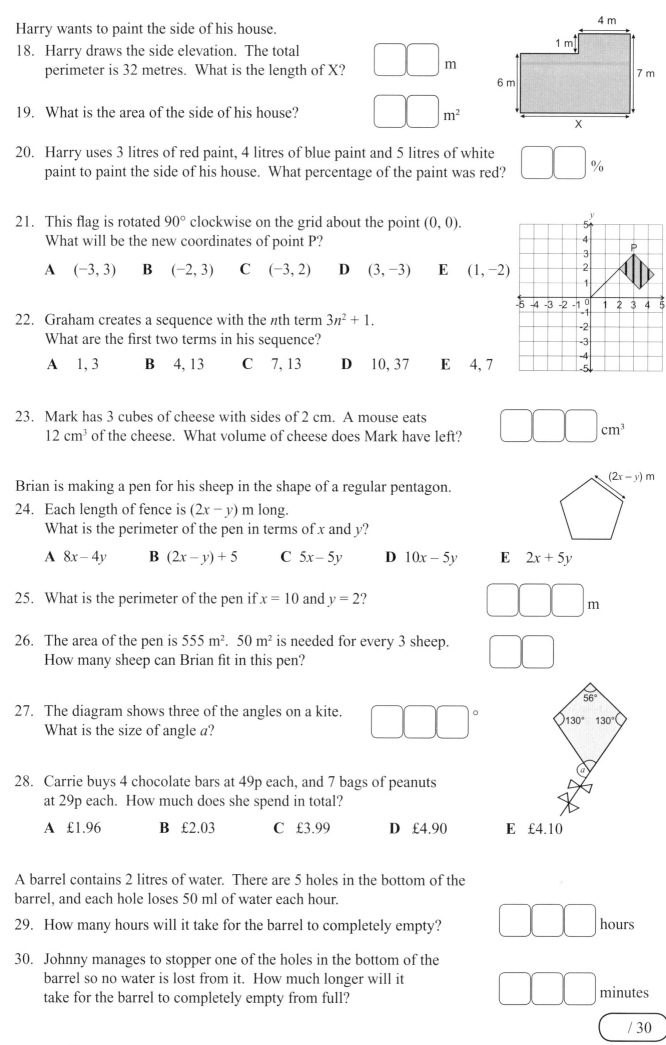

Harry wants to paint the side of his house.

18. Harry draws the side elevation. The total perimeter is 32 metres. What is the length of X? ⬚⬚ m

19. What is the area of the side of his house? ⬚⬚ m²

20. Harry uses 3 litres of red paint, 4 litres of blue paint and 5 litres of white paint to paint the side of his house. What percentage of the paint was red? ⬚⬚ %

21. This flag is rotated 90° clockwise on the grid about the point (0, 0). What will be the new coordinates of point P?

    A (−3, 3)   B (−2, 3)   C (−3, 2)   D (3, −3)   E (1, −2)

22. Graham creates a sequence with the *n*th term $3n^2 + 1$. What are the first two terms in his sequence?

    A 1, 3   B 4, 13   C 7, 13   D 10, 37   E 4, 7

23. Mark has 3 cubes of cheese with sides of 2 cm. A mouse eats 12 cm³ of the cheese. What volume of cheese does Mark have left? ⬚⬚⬚ cm³

Brian is making a pen for his sheep in the shape of a regular pentagon.

24. Each length of fence is $(2x - y)$ m long. What is the perimeter of the pen in terms of *x* and *y*?

    A 8x – 4y   B (2x – y) + 5   C 5x – 5y   D 10x – 5y   E 2x + 5y

25. What is the perimeter of the pen if *x* = 10 and *y* = 2? ⬚⬚⬚ m

26. The area of the pen is 555 m². 50 m² is needed for every 3 sheep. How many sheep can Brian fit in this pen? ⬚⬚

27. The diagram shows three of the angles on a kite. What is the size of angle *a*? ⬚⬚⬚ °

28. Carrie buys 4 chocolate bars at 49p each, and 7 bags of peanuts at 29p each. How much does she spend in total?

    A £1.96   B £2.03   C £3.99   D £4.90   E £4.10

A barrel contains 2 litres of water. There are 5 holes in the bottom of the barrel, and each hole loses 50 ml of water each hour.

29. How many hours will it take for the barrel to completely empty? ⬚⬚⬚ hours

30. Johnny manages to stopper one of the holes in the bottom of the barrel so no water is lost from it. How much longer will it take for the barrel to completely empty from full? ⬚⬚⬚ minutes

/ 30

Assessment Test 3

Allow 10 minutes to do Section A and 25 minutes to do Section B.
Work as quickly and as carefully as you can.

You can print **multiple-choice answer sheets** for these questions from our website — go to
www.cgplearning.co.uk/11+. If you'd prefer to answer them in write-in format, either write
your answers in the spaces provided or circle the **correct answer** from the options given.

Section A — Quick Maths

You have **10 minutes** to complete this section.
There are **30 questions** in this section.

1. Each of the small squares in the shape on the right has an area of 1 cm².
    What is the total area of the shape? ⬚⬚.⬚⬚ cm²

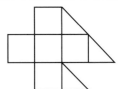

2. Which unit is most suitable for measuring the length of a football pitch?

    A   centimetres   **C**   metres   **E**   litres
    B   millimetres   **D**   kilometres

3. Elsa counts the vehicles that pass her school during
    her lunchtime. The pictogram shows her results.
    How many buses did she see? ⬚⬚

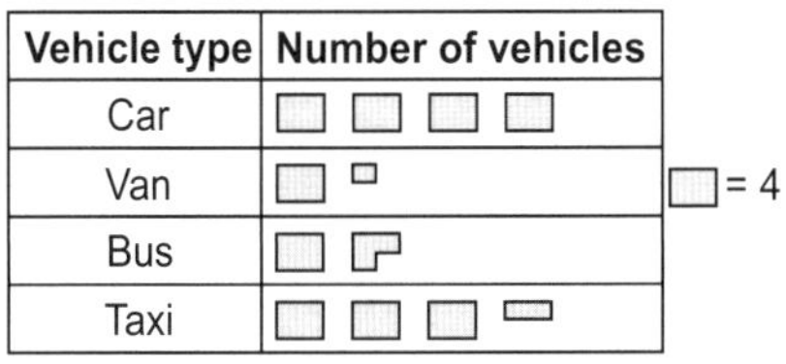

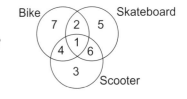

Vehicle type	Number of vehicles
Car	⬚ ⬚ ⬚ ⬚
Van	⬚ ▫
Bus	⬚ ⬚
Taxi	⬚ ⬚ ⬚ ▭

⬚ = 4

4. The Venn diagram on the right shows how many children
    in a class have bikes, skateboards and scooters.
    How many children have a skateboard and a scooter, but not a bike? ⬚⬚

5. Which of the shapes to the right has
    exactly one pair of parallel sides?

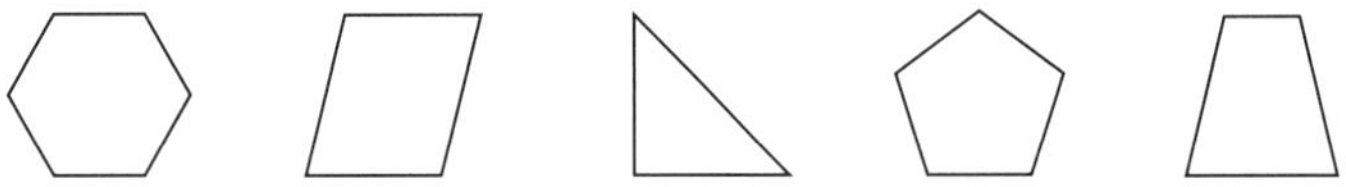

    A   **B**   **C**   **D**   **E**

6. Robert is meeting a friend at 13:45. What is this time written in the 12-hour clock?

    A 1:45 pm   **B** 2:45 am   **C** 1:45 am   **D** 3:45 pm   **E** 2:45 pm

7. How many lines of symmetry does a regular octagon have?

    A 2   **B** 4   **C** 6   **D** 8   **E** 10

8. This chart shows the number of boys and girls in each
    year group in a school. How many
    children are in the biggest year group? ⬚⬚⬚

Year Group	Boys	Girls
2	49	50
3	52	56
4	55	57
5	54	59
6	35	54

9. Isla works out that 90 × 80 = 7200. ⬚⬚.⬚⬚
    What is 90 × 0.08?

Carry on to the next question →→

	Price
Coleslaw	25p
Green Salad	80p
Tomato Salad	40p
Rice Salad	50p
Potato Salad	45p
Jacket Potato	99p
Rice	85p

10. Which is the most likely mass of a tin of soup?

   A 0.4 g   **B** 400 g   **C** 40 kg   **D** 4 kg   **E** 4 g

11. Maddy buys a tomato salad, some coleslaw and a jacket potato.
    How much change will she receive from a £5 note?

   A £1.64   **B** £2.16   **C** £3.36   **D** £3.60   **E** £3.63

12. Look at these fractions.

   $\frac{7}{20}$ $\frac{3}{4}$ $\frac{1}{5}$ $\frac{3}{20}$ $\frac{5}{20}$

   Which of the following shows them arranged from smallest to largest?

   A $\frac{3}{20}, \frac{1}{5}, \frac{5}{20}, \frac{3}{4}, \frac{7}{20}$ **D** $\frac{3}{4}, \frac{7}{20}, \frac{5}{20}, \frac{1}{5}, \frac{3}{20}$

   B $\frac{3}{20}, \frac{1}{5}, \frac{5}{20}, \frac{7}{20}, \frac{3}{4}$ **E** $\frac{1}{5}, \frac{3}{20}, \frac{5}{20}, \frac{7}{20}, \frac{3}{4}$

   C $\frac{3}{20}, \frac{3}{4}, \frac{1}{5}, \frac{5}{20}, \frac{7}{20}$

13. The chart on the right shows the proportions of boys and girls
    in the chess club and the computer club. There are
    30 children in each club. How many more
    boys than girls are there in the computer club?

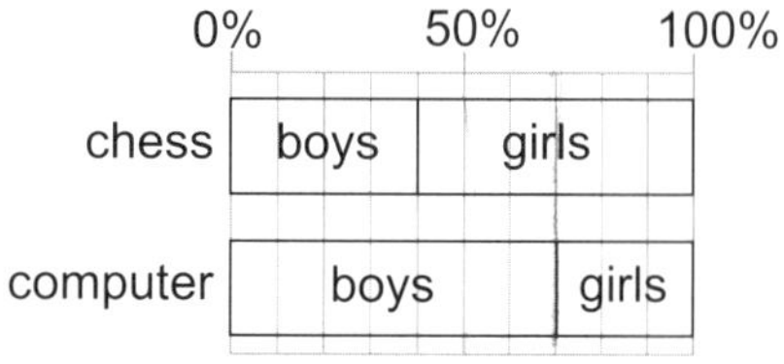

Name	Time
Betsy	4 mins 18 secs
Cara	3 mins 59 secs
Ian	4 mins 2 secs
Sian	4 mins 20 secs
Tony	4 mins 27 secs

14. A group of children have a competition to see who is fastest at
    running a cross country race. The results are shown in the table
    on the right. Who came second?

   A Betsy   **B** Cara   **C** Ian   **D** Sian   **E** Tony

15. John thinks of a number. He multiplies it by 11 and subtracts 9.
    The answer he gets is 112. What number did he start with?

16. What is the probability of throwing a number greater than 4 on a fair, six-sided dice?

   A $\frac{1}{6}$ **B** $\frac{5}{6}$ **C** $\frac{1}{2}$ **D** $\frac{1}{3}$ **E** $\frac{2}{3}$

17. Jenny is standing facing north at the point marked X on the grid.
    She moves 3 units forward, then makes an anti-clockwise
    turn through 135°. Which letter is she now facing?

   A   **B**   **C**   **D**   **E**

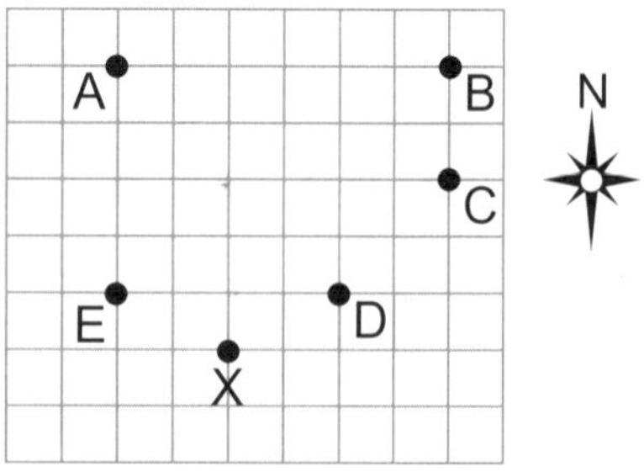

18. Sasha starts her homework at 4:20 pm. She can stop and go
    to visit her friend when she has done $1\frac{3}{4}$ hours of homework.
    What time can she visit her friend?

    ☐☐:☐☐ pm

19. Sarah has run a total distance of 168 km over a 12 week period.
    How far does she run each day if she runs the same distance each day?

    ☐☐☐ km

Carry on to the next question → →

20. Which diagram shows how the 3-dimensional shape to the right would look when viewed from directly above?

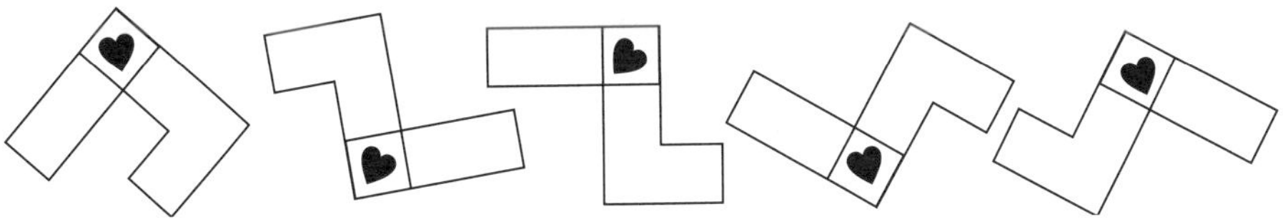

A   B   C   D   E

21. The perimeter of a rectangular floor tile is 120 cm. The length of the tile is 20 cm greater than its width. What is its width in centimetres?

☐☐ cm

22. The temperature of a patient at 9 am each day was recorded and plotted on a graph. What is the range of the temperatures?

☐.☐☐ °C

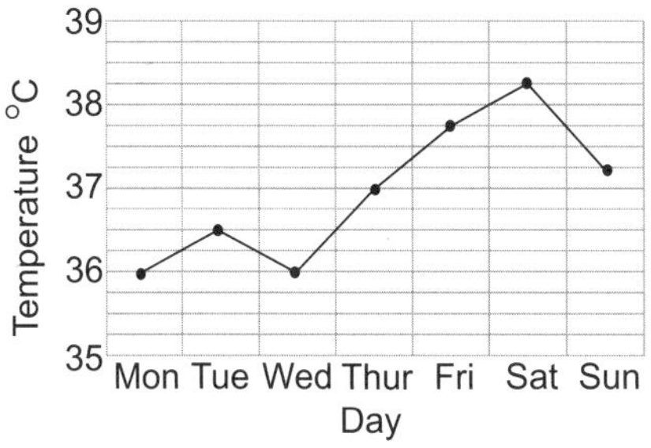

23. Luke starts a sequence at –5 and counts up in steps of 1.5. Which of the following numbers does he count?

   A –1   **B** 0   **C** 2   **D** 3   **E** 4

24. Ben makes this pattern by repeating three shapes over and over again. How many hearts will there be in the first 20 shapes?

   A 6   **B** 7   **C** 3   **D** 8   **E** 4

   ♥ ◠ ✚ ♥ ◠ ✚ ...

25. Sue's car uses 5 full tanks of petrol to travel 2985 miles. How many miles can she travel on one full tank of petrol?

☐☐☐☐ miles

26. Poppy is investigating a pattern made of squares. How many squares will be in shape 11 of the pattern?

☐☐

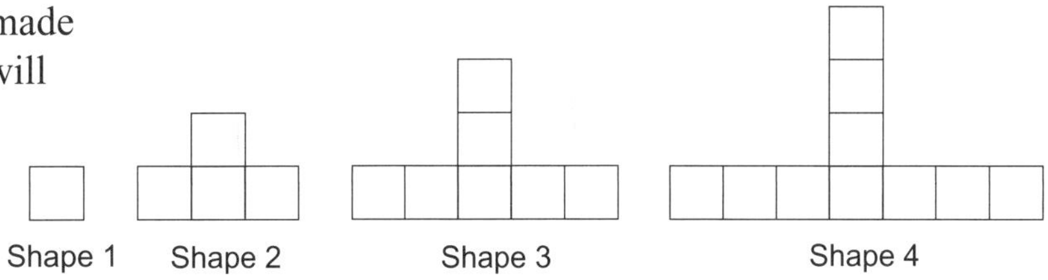

Shape 1   Shape 2   Shape 3   Shape 4

27. 1.75 pints = 1 litre. How many pint bottles would you need to hold 6 litres of water?

☐☐

28. Which statement below is true about the spinner on the right?

   A   It is equally likely to land on an odd or even number.
   B   There is an even chance of it landing on a number greater than 4.
   C   The probability of it landing on 2 is $\frac{1}{8}$.
   D   The probability of it landing on an even number is $\frac{1}{3}$.
   E   The probability of it landing on a number less than 3 is $\frac{1}{2}$.

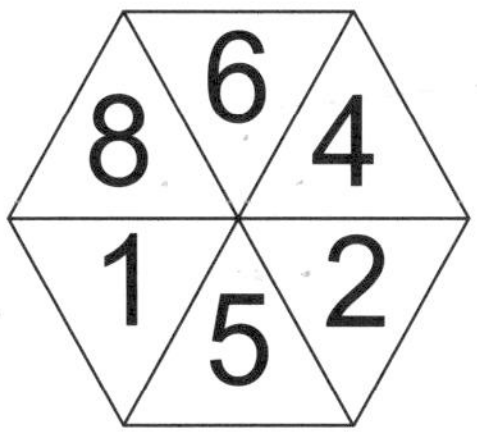

29. Alice buys a 500 ml bottle of shampoo. She uses 125 ml in one week. What faction of the shampoo is left in the bottle?

   A $\frac{1}{4}$ **B** $\frac{1}{2}$ **C** $\frac{1}{3}$ **D** $\frac{3}{4}$ **E** $\frac{2}{3}$

30. The coordinates of 3 corners of a rectangle are (4, 2), (4, 10) and (8, 10). What are the coordinates of the fourth corner?

(☐☐ , ☐☐)

/ 30

Assessment Test 3

Section B — Long Maths

You have **25 minutes** to complete this section.
There are **30 questions** in this section.

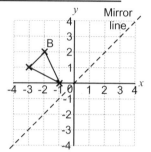

1. The shape on the grid is reflected in the mirror line.
   What are the coordinates of the image of point B?

   A (−2, 2)   **B** (3, −2)   **C** (1, −3)   **D** (2, −2)   **E** (−1, −3)

2. The ages in months of four out of six babies at a clinic are given below.

6	3	8	2

   The median age of these four babies is 4.5 months.
   The median age of the 6 babies is also 4.5 months.
   Which of the following could be the ages in months of the fifth and sixth babies?

   A 8 and 12   **B** 1 and 2   **C** 2 and 8   **D** 11 and 12   **E** 3 and 4

James records the weather for 20 days. He draws a pie chart of his results.

3. It was foggy for 3 days. What size angle should he draw to represent this?
   A 90°   **B** 54°   **C** 36°   **D** 45°   **E** 180°

4. James draws an angle of 108° to correspond to the number of days on
   which it rained. Out of the 20 days James recorded, on how many did it rain?

Veronica has an empty cardboard box which is shaped like a perfect cube.

5. What is the sum of the numbers of faces,
   edges and vertices of the box?

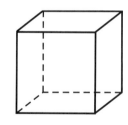

6. The volume of the cube is 216 cm³.
   What is the length of one edge? cm

7. A printer uses the following formula to work out the cost, *C*, in pounds, of printing *m* leaflets:
   $$C = 15(m \div 100) + 5.$$
   How much will it cost, in pounds, to have 300 leaflets printed?   £

8. Caleb pours $\frac{2}{5}$ of a litre of water out of a full 10 litre bucket.
   How many millilitres are left in the bucket?

   A 9500 ml   **B** 9600 ml   **C** 600 ml   **D** 9400 ml   **E** 400 ml

Ben is mixing feed for rabbits. The recipe states to mix 1 part of
vegetables to 3 parts of hay and 5 parts of rabbit flakes by weight.

9. Ben makes a mix using 7.5 kg of rabbit flakes.
   How many kg of hay will he need?  kg

10. Ben makes another mix which has 3.5 kg of vegetables in it.
    What is the total weight of this mix in kilograms?  kg

Carry on to the next question → →

Paul is a ferryman. He counts the number of children and adults that use his ferry over the course of one week. He records his results on a bar graph.

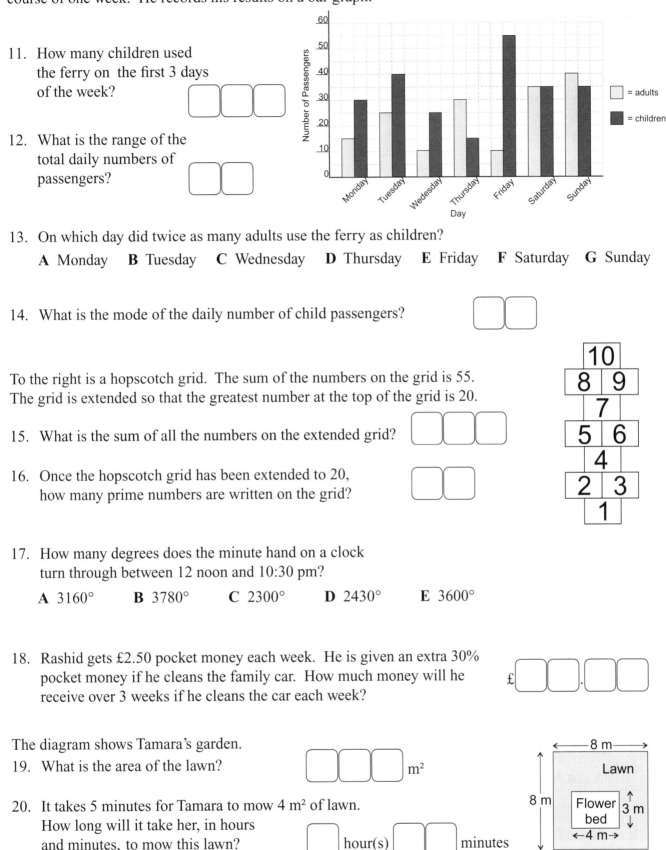

11. How many children used the ferry on the first 3 days of the week?

12. What is the range of the total daily numbers of passengers?

13. On which day did twice as many adults use the ferry as children?

    A Monday   **B** Tuesday   **C** Wednesday   **D** Thursday   **E** Friday   **F** Saturday   **G** Sunday

14. What is the mode of the daily number of child passengers?

To the right is a hopscotch grid. The sum of the numbers on the grid is 55.
The grid is extended so that the greatest number at the top of the grid is 20.

15. What is the sum of all the numbers on the extended grid?

16. Once the hopscotch grid has been extended to 20, how many prime numbers are written on the grid?

17. How many degrees does the minute hand on a clock turn through between 12 noon and 10:30 pm?

    A 3160°   **B** 3780°   **C** 2300°   **D** 2430°   **E** 3600°

18. Rashid gets £2.50 pocket money each week. He is given an extra 30% pocket money if he cleans the family car. How much money will he receive over 3 weeks if he cleans the car each week?

The diagram shows Tamara's garden.

19. What is the area of the lawn?   m²

20. It takes 5 minutes for Tamara to mow 4 m² of lawn. How long will it take her, in hours and minutes, to mow this lawn?   hour(s)   minutes

21. Ian buys 6 sandwiches costing £1.99 each and 3 drinks costing 49p each.
He does this calculation to estimate the cost: 6 × £2 + 3 × £0.50
How does his estimate differ from the exact cost?

    A £12 too much   **C** 12p too little   **E** 6p too much

    B 9p too much   **D** 9p too little

Carry on to the next question → →

22. Sleeping bags are given a rating to show the minimum temperature they can be used at:

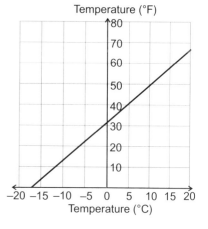

Temperature (°F)

Sleeping bag rating	1	2	3	4	5
Minimum temperature (°C)	5	0	−5	−10	−15

Adam needs to buy a sleeping bag that he can use at 25 °F.
The graph on the right can be used to change a temperature in °F to a temperature in °C.
What is the lowest rating of sleeping bag he can buy?

Susan has a bag containing 60 marbles. 25% of them are red, 30% of them are blue and 15% of them are green. The remaining marbles are yellow.

23. How many yellow marbles are in the bag?

24. Susan takes a marble out of the bag at random. What is the probability it will be green?

   A $\frac{1}{4}$　　**B** $\frac{5}{6}$　　**C** $\frac{3}{20}$　　**D** $\frac{1}{10}$　　**E** $\frac{1}{5}$

25. Heather is packing a tent to take on holiday and wants to work out how big it is inside. She chooses to model it as a regular triangular prism.

   Volume of a triangular prism = area of triangular side × length

   What is the volume of Heather's tent?　　m³

   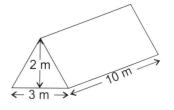

26. A school holds a concert. There are 42 rows of 48 seats. How many seats are there?

27. This table shows the number of children in 6 different classes. What is the mean number of children?

Class	6A	6B	6C	6D	6E	6F
Number of children	16	16	11	17	12	12

28. On Saturday April 23rd, Claire's father tells her that it is 6 weeks until they go on holiday. They are going on holiday on a Saturday. What date will this be?

   A 1st June　　**B** 2nd June　　**C** 3rd June　　**D** 4th June　　**E** 5th June

Russell wins £500 in a prize draw.

29. He spends £260 on a new computer, and decides to buy some games that cost £39.99 each. Which expression gives the amount of money Russell will have left if he buys n games?

   A $240n$　　**B** $500 - 260n$　　**C** $240 + 39.99n$　　**D** $240 - 39.99n$　　**E** $500 - 39.99n$

30. What is the highest number of computer games Russell can buy from his winnings, after purchasing his new computer?

   / 30

Assessment Test 4

Allow 10 minutes to do Section A and 25 minutes to do Section B.
Work as quickly and as carefully as you can.

You can print **multiple-choice answer sheets** for these questions from our website — go to
www.cgplearning.co.uk/11+. If you'd prefer to answer them in write-in format, either write
your answers in the spaces provided or circle the **correct answer** from the options given.

Section A — Quick Maths
You have **10 minutes** to complete this section.
There are **30 questions** in this section.

1. What is the value of the 7 in 7 230 000?
    A   seven hundred million   **C**   seventy thousand   **E**   seven million
    B   seven hundred thousand   **D**   seventy million

2. Which of the following is most likely to be the height of a fully grown tree?
    A   12 metres   **C**   1.2 centimetres   **E**   0.12 metres
    B   12 millimetres   **D**   0.12 centimetres

3. Tallulah has drawn a trapezium.

    She reflects her shape in the dotted mirror line shown to make a new shape.
    What type of shape does she form?

    A   pentagon   **C**   heptagon   **E**   quadrilateral
    B   octagon   **D**   hexagon

4. Courtney records the temperature
    each day for five days.

Day	Monday	Tuesday	Wednesday	Thursday	Friday
Temperature	−2 °C	1 °C	0 °C	2 °C	−1 °C

    On which day does she record the lowest temperature?

    A   Monday   **B**   Tuesday   **C**   Wednesday   **D**   Thursday   **E**   Friday

5. Ted's favourite TV programme is shown in the evening.
    It starts and finishes at the times shown on the clocks.

    How long does the programme last for?

    ☐☐ hour(s) ☐☐ minutes

    Start   Finish

6. Maxie draws this rectangle in her maths book.
    What is the area of the rectangle?

    7 cm   2.5 cm   ☐☐.☐ cm²

7. Which of these numbers is smallest?

    A 0.81   **B** 1.92   **C** 12.4   **D** 21.42   **E** 0.18

8. A regular heptagon has a perimeter of 56 cm.
    How long is each side?

    ☐☐ cm

    Carry on to the next question → →

9. Kate buys a second-hand car for £3,080.
The original cost of the car was £6,999.
By how much has the car's value decreased?   £

10. How much does the kitten on the right weigh?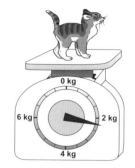

    A 2.5 kg   **C** 2.25 kg   **E** 2.125 kg
    B 2.05 kg   **D** 0.5 kg

11. Joe eats three loaves of bread on a seven day holiday.
He eats the same amount of bread each day.
What fraction of a loaf does he eat each day of the holiday?

    A $\frac{1}{7}$ **B** $\frac{3}{7}$ **C** $\frac{1}{4}$ **D** $\frac{4}{7}$ **E** $\frac{1}{3}$

12. This pie chart shows the pets belonging to the children in Sue's class.
The total number of pets in the survey is 32.

    Which of the following is the best estimate for
    the number of dogs owned by the class?

    A 8   **B** 15   **C** 18   **D** 6   **E** 9

    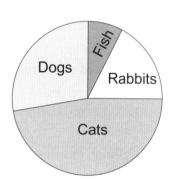

13. Li estimates the answer to 39 × 43 by rounding both numbers to
the nearest 10 before multiplying them. What answer should he get?

    A 1500   **B** 1600   **C** 1200   **D** 2000   **E** 1677

14. Lucas lives in Kneesall.
He needs to be at Rippen
by 8:40 am to go on a trip.

    The timetable shows the bus times.

Bus depot	8:00 am	8:05 am	8:10 am	8:15 am	8:20 am
Kneesall	8:10 am	8:15 am	8:20 am	8:25 am	8:30 am
Rippen	8:15 am	8:20 am	8:25 am	8:30 am	8:35 am
Hathern	8:29 am	8:34 am	8:39 am	8:44 am	8:49 am

    What is the latest time he can catch a bus?    am

15. Gus has a piece of ribbon that is 48 m long.
He cuts it into pieces that are each $\frac{1}{3}$ m long.
How many pieces are there?

16. Rashid is thinking of a 3D shape. The shape has 4 faces, 4 vertices and 6 edges.
Which of the following could Rashid's shape be?

    A square-based pyramid   **C** triangular prism   **E** cylinder
    B triangular-based pyramid   **D** cube

17. 30 × 806 = 24 180

    What is 30 × 403?

    A 1209   **B** 12 900   **C** 48 360   **D** 4836   **E** 12 090

18. Which of these is the best estimate for the size of angle x?

    A 100°   **B** 90°   **C** 80°   **D** 135°   **E** 180°

    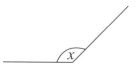

Carry on to the next question →→

19. Jonathan's family go on a journey which is shown on this graph. The family stops for a break. How long does the break last for?

    A 1½ hours **B** 1 hour **C** ¾ hour **D** ½ hour **E** 1¾ hours

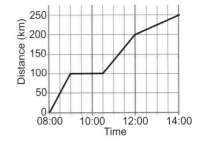

20. Class 7 have made 250 biscuits to sell at the school fair. They pack them in bags of 12.

    How many biscuits are left over?

21. Mark takes seven 4 cm cubes and places them end to end to make this shape.

    He then puts the shape on a piece of paper, and draws around it with a pencil.

    What is the perimeter of the shape that he draws? ☐☐☐ cm

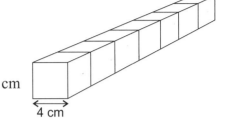

4 cm

22. A bag contains 5 cherry sweets and 10 lime sweets. What is the probability of randomly picking a cherry sweet?

    A $\frac{5}{10}$ **B** $\frac{10}{15}$ **C** $\frac{1}{3}$ **D** $\frac{1}{2}$ **E** $\frac{3}{4}$

23. The pictogram shows the number of awards Class 7 gained each day in a week.

    What is the modal number of awards in a day?

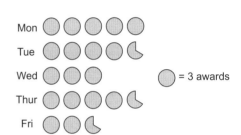

24. A bag contains some striped and spotted balls. The pattern on the balls is either red or yellow. The sorting diagram shows how many of each ball there are.

    Which type of ball is most likely to be pulled out at random?

	spotted	striped
yellow	6	3
red	4	7

    A a red ball   **C** a striped ball   **E** a red striped ball
    B a yellow ball   **D** a spotted ball

25. Bilal is drawing a parallelogram on a coordinate grid. Points A, B and C are three of the corners of the parallelogram. Which of these could be the coordinates of the fourth corner of the parallelogram?

    A (2 , 2) **B** (4 , 2) **C** (1 , 2) **D** (3 , 2) **E** (2 , 3)

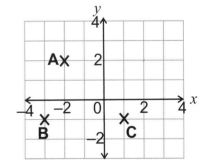

26. $x^2 - 1 > 49$

    If x is a positive whole number, what is the smallest it could be?

27. Which expression can be used to work out the nth term of this series?

    −1   1   3   5   7

    A $3n$ **B** $n - 3$ **C** $2n - 3$ **D** $2 \div n - 3$ **E** $2n + 3$

    Carry on to the next question → →

    Assessment Test 4

28. The net to the right folds up to form a 3-dimensional shape.
What is the volume of this shape?

☐☐ cm³

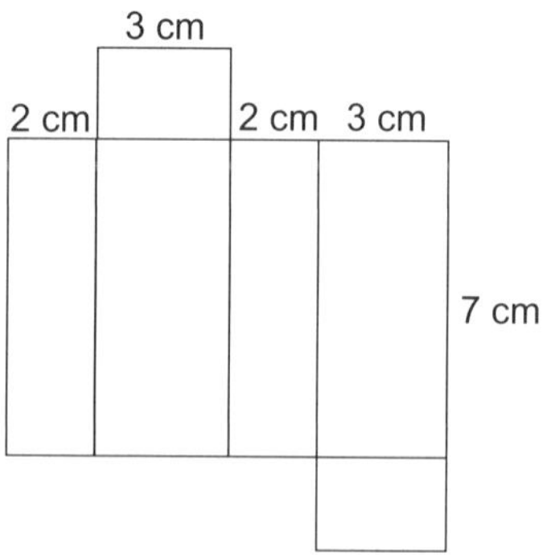

3 cm

2 cm   *2 cm*   *3 cm*

7 cm

29. Lucy wants to buy a T-shirt in a sale.
All items in the sale are reduced by 60%.

What is the sale price of the T-shirt if the original price was £n?

A $n \div 60$ **B** $\frac{2}{5}(n)$ **C** $n - 60$ **D** $\frac{3}{5}(n)$ **E** $2n - 6$

30. Oscar faces north and then turns through 225° in a clockwise direction.
Which direction is he now facing?

A west   **B** south-west   **C** south-east   **D** south   **E** east

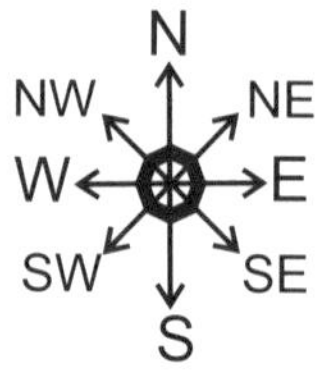

N
NW   NE
W ← ✳ → E
SW   SE
S

(/ 30)

Section B — Long Maths
You have **25 minutes** to complete this section.
There are **30 questions** in this section.

---

1. Look at the volumes shown below. What is the total volume when they are added together?

5.555 litres   5.55 litres   5.5 litres   5.0 litres   0.5 litres

☐☐.☐☐☐ litres

A school buys some badges to sell.

2. Children in Class 1B are divided into groups to sell the badges.
There are 4 boys and 3 girls in each group. There are 15 girls in Class 1B.
How many children are there in the class?

☐☐

3. The school pays 70p for each badge and sells them for £1 each.
The school sells all the badges, and makes a profit of £60.
How many badges did the school buy?

☐☐☐

4. Look at the function machine on the right.
If the number 25 comes out of
the machine, what number went in?

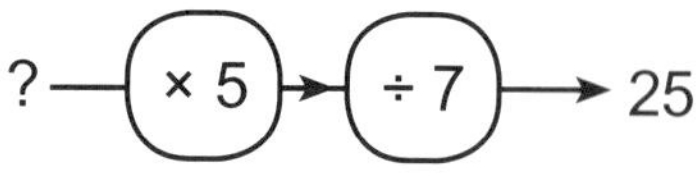

☐☐☐☐

? —(× 5)—(÷ 7)→ 25

Macy and Carol visit a bakery.

5. Macy buys four sandwiches. One of the sandwiches costs £1.99.
The other three sandwiches cost £1.49 each. What is the total cost of the sandwiches?

A £6.59   **B** £6.46   **C** £5.56   **D** £5.64   **E** £6.54

6. Carol buys 3 jam donuts and two sausage rolls.
Each sausage roll costs 92p. She spends £3.79.
How much does one jam donut cost?

☐☐☐ p

7. Carol also wants to buy some cakes. Which of the following is the cheapest price per cake?

A 15p each   **B** 3 for 39p   **C** 10 for £1   **D** 25 for £2   **E** 15 for £1.50

8. Find the sum of all the square numbers between 46 and 91.

☐☐☐☐

Carry on to the next question →→

9. The diagram shows a patio made from two identical triangular slabs.
   What is the area of the patio?

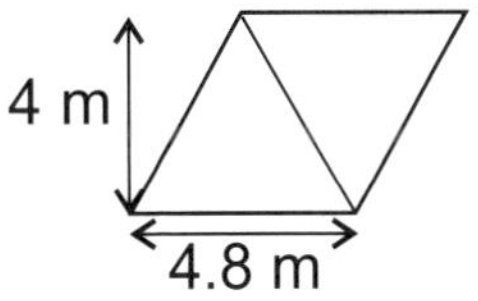

   A 3.84 m²   **C** 9.6 m²   **E** 192 m²

   B 19.2 m²   **D** 38.4 m²

   4 m

   4.8 m

10. The frequency chart shows the results of throwing a dice.
    How many times was the dice thrown altogether?

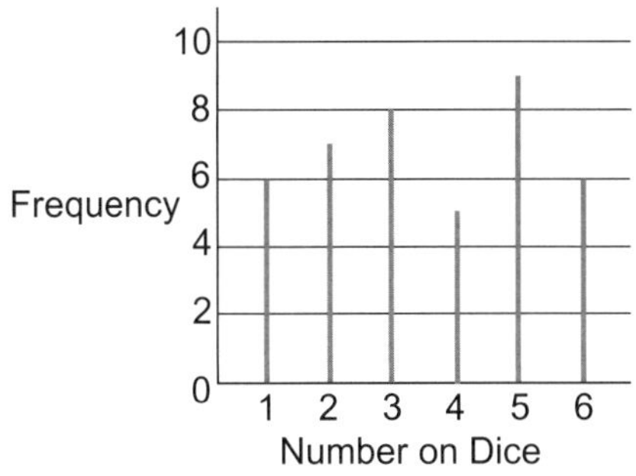

    Frequency

    Number on Dice

A dog eats 245 g of dried food per meal. She has 3 meals per day.

11. How much food does the dog eat in a week?

    A 0.4725 kg   **B** 5.145 kg   **C** 3.375 kg   **D** 1.575 kg   **E** 47.25 kg

12. The dog's owner buys the food in 1.25 kg bags. How many full meals does one bag provide?

    A 3   **B** 4   **C** 5   **D** 10   **E** 12

The table shows the opening times of Mr Jason's café. The cost of running the café is £10 per hour and the café is open 7 days a week.

13. How much more per week does it cost to run the café in the summer than in the winter?

    £

	Opens	Closes
Mar – Sep	9 am	6 pm
Oct – Feb	11 am	4 pm

14. Mr Jason surveys 550 visitors to his café about their eating habits.
    He finds that 4% of the visitors are vegetarian.
    What number of the visitors are vegetarian?

15. The diagram shows a regular octagon.
    What size is angle x?

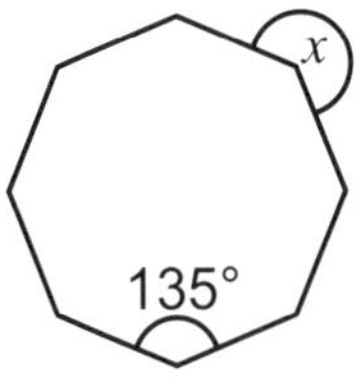

    °

    x

    135°

16. A caterer is making a sauce. She uses 4.5 kg of apples for every 2 kg of sugar.
    How many kilograms of apples will she need if she uses 9 kg of sugar?

    A 4 kg   **B** 202.5 kg   **C** 2.025 kg   **D** 0.25 kg   **E** 20.25 kg

This chart shows the masses of some bags of fruit on sale in a supermarket.
Kai buys 1 bag of oranges, 2 bags of bananas, 3 bags of apples and 1 bag of pears.

Fruit	Mass per bag (g)
Oranges	600
Bananas	450
Apples	500
Pears	750

17. How many kilograms of fruit has he bought?

    . kg

18. Altogether Kai gets 8 bananas.
    What is the average mass of one banana?

    . g

19. Simon is investigating patterns made from triangles.
    Which expression represents the number of small triangles in the nth pattern in the series?

    A $n + 1$ **B** $n^2 + 1$ **C** n **D** n^2 **E** $n^2 - 1$

    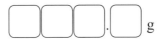

    Pattern 1   Pattern 2   Pattern 3   Pattern 4   Pattern 5

    Carry on to the next question → →

    Assessment Test 4

70

20. Adam starts watching a film at 10:45 am.
The film lasts for 136 minutes.
What time does the film finish?

☐☐:☐☐ pm

21. Katie buys six 1 litre cartons of milk each week. She drinks 350 ml of milk twice a day.
She uses the whole carton before she opens a new one.
How much milk will be left over after 7 days?

☐☐☐☐ ml

Jasmine builds this model on a table.
Each brick has a volume of 3 cm³.

22. What is the total volume of the model?

☐☐☐ cm³

23. What fraction of the number of blocks in the model are not touching the table?

A ⅓ **B** ¾ **C** ⅖ **D** 5⁄7 **E** ⅗

24. Jack is cooking a turkey that weighs 2.2 kg. To work out how many
minutes he needs to cook it for he is using the formula 20w + 70.
w is the weight of the turkey in kg.

How long does Jack need to cook his turkey for?

☐☐☐ minutes

25. Roddy is playing a computer game.
The time taken to complete each level is shown in the table.
The mean time it takes him to complete each level is 42 minutes.
How long did it take him to complete level 4?

Level	1	2	3	4	5
Minutes	31	36	44		52

☐☐☐ minutes

26. The table shows how much money Ahmed saves
each month. What is Ahmed's mean monthly
saving for these 6 months?

£ ☐☐.☐☐

January	£1.20
February	80p
March	£1.50
April	£1.10
May	£1.50
June	50p

27. Roger wants to spread grass seed on a rectangular area of soil.
A tub of seed costs £5.99 and covers 12 square metres of soil.

How much will the seed cost altogether if Roger's area of soil
measures 8 metres by 6 metres?

£ ☐☐.☐☐

Look at the information on the right for a breakfast cereal.

A 30 gram serving contains:

Protein	4 g
Carbohydrate	21 g
Fat	1.5 g
Fibre	0.8 g
Salt	0.5 g

28. How much carbohydrate would be
in a 20 gram serving of cereal?

☐☐ g

29. How many grams of the breakfast cereal
would you need to eat to get 2 g of fibre?

☐☐ g

30. What percentage of the breakfast cereal is fat?

A 20% **B** 15% **C** 50% **D** 5% **E** 0.5% **F** 0.2% **G** 1.5%

/ 30

M6QDE1

Assessment Test 4

13. £2700
£2.70 = 1 pack. In a box there are 100 packs, so that will cost £2.70 × 100 = £270
Mrs Chapman buys 10 boxes, so that will cost £270 × 10 = £2700

14. 26 300
Ampney's population is 2630. Bentley's population is 10 times smaller than Ampney's, 2630 ÷ 10 = 263.
Clifton's population is 1000 times larger than Bentley's, 263 × 1000 = 263 000
Dannett's population is 10 times smaller than Clifton's, 263 000 ÷ 10 = 26 300

Pages 7-8

You could use partitioning to find the answers to these multiplications. Break up one number into units, tens, hundreds, etc. and multiply each of the parts with the other number, one at a time — then add them together. You could also set the numbers out in columns and multiply them or use the grid method.

1. 104
13 breaks into 10 + 3. 10 × 8 = 80
3 × 8 = 24, 80 + 24 = 104

2. 216
24 breaks into 20 + 4. 20 × 9 = 180
4 × 9 = 36, 180 + 36 = 216

3. 238
It's often easier to use columns when multiplying two 2-digit numbers:

```
        1 7
  ×     1 4
    ─────────
        6 8     (17 × 4)
        2
  + 1 7 0       (17 × 10)
    ─────────
      2 3 8
        1
```

4. 1650
330 breaks into 300 + 30
300 × 5 = 1500, 30 × 5 = 150
1500 + 150 = 1650

5. 1430
It's often easier to use columns when multiplying two 2-digit numbers:

```
          6 5
    ×     2 2
      ─────────
        1 3 0     (65 × 2)
          1
    + 1 3 0 0     (65 × 20)
          1
      ─────────
      1 4 3 0
```

6. 752
```
          4 7
    ×     1 6
      ─────────
        2 8 2     (47 × 6)
          4
    + 4 7 0       (47 × 10)
      ─────────
        7 5 2
          1
```

7. 21.6
3.6 breaks into 3 + 0.6. 6 × 3 = 18
6 × 0.6 = 3.6, 18 + 3.6 = 21.6

8. 29.4
4.2 breaks into 4 + 0.2. 7 × 4 = 28
7 × 0.2 = 1.4, 28 + 1.4 = 29.4

9. 74.4
9.3 breaks into 9 + 0.3. 8 × 9 = 72
8 × 0.3 = 2.4, 72 + 2.4 = 74.4

10. 448
6.4 breaks into 6 + 0.4. 70 × 6 = 420,
70 × 0.4 = 28, 420 + 28 = 448

11. 26.4
2.2 breaks into 2 + 0.2. 12 × 2 = 24,
12 × 0.2 = 2.4, 24 + 2.4 = 26.4

12. 1.15
0.23 breaks into 0.2 + 0.03.
5 × 0.2 = 1, 5 × 0.03 = 0.15, 1 + 0.15 = 1.15

13. £7.80
Round £1.95 to £2, by adding 5p.
4 × 2 = 8, then minus the 20p (4 × 5p) you added when rounding: £8 – 20p = £7.80

14. £11.50
You need to work out £2.30 × 5.
2.30 breaks into 2 + 0.3.
5 × 2 = 10, 0.3 × 5 = 1.5,
10 + 1.5 = 11.5 = £11.50

15. £271
The cost for 5 adults to go swimming is £11.50.
5 × 10 = 50. So the takings from 50 adults were £11.50 × 10 = £115
The cost for 4 children to go swimming is £7.80. The cost for 8 children to go swimming is £7.80 × 2. 7.80 breaks into 7 + 0.8.
2 × 7 = 14 and 2 × 0.8 = 1.6.
14 + 1.6 = 15.6 = £15.60. So the takings from 80 children were £15.60 × 10 = £156
The total takings were £115 + £156 = £271
Alternatively, work out the answers from scratch. So the takings from adults were:
£2.30 × 50 = £2.30 × 10 × 5
= £23.00 × 5 = £115
The takings from children were:
£1.95 × 80 = (£2 × 80) – (5p × 80)
= £160 – £4 = £156
The total takings were £115 + £156 = £271

16. 168.48
To get from 3.24 to 32.4 you multiply by 10. To get from 52 to 5.2 you divide by 10. So, the answer to 32.4 × 5.2 is the same as 3.24 × 52, which is 168.48.

17. D
Use estimation to do this calculation.
7.7 rounds up to 8 and 6.4 rounds down to 6.
8 × 6 = 48.
The closest answer to this is option D, 49.28.

18. 189
There are 21 days in 3 weeks so you need to work out 21 × 9. 21 breaks into 20 + 1.
20 × 9 = 180. 1 × 9 = 9, 180 + 9 = 189

19. 225
2.5 breaks into 2 + 0.5. 90 × 2 = 180,
90 × 0.5 = 45, 180 + 45 = 225.

20. 50 384
188 is double 94, so the answer will be double 25 192.

```
      2 5 1 9 2
    ×         2
      ─────────
      5 0 3 8 4
          1 1
```

21. C
Work each calculation out by ignoring the zeros, and multiplying the digits at the beginning of each number. Finally, put the same number of zeros that you ignored on the end of the answer.
A: 6 × 4000: 6 × 4 = 24. Three zeros have been ignored, so 6 × 4000 = 24 000
B: 70 × 300: 7 × 3 = 21. Three zeros have been ignored, so 70 × 300 = 21 000
C: 200 × 200: 2 × 2 = 4. Four zeros have been ignored, so 200 × 200 = 40 000.
D: 900 × 10: 9 × 1 = 9. Three zeros have been ignored, so 900 × 10 = 9000
E: 8 × 500: 8 × 5 = 40. Two zeros have been ignored, so 8 × 500 = 4000
C was the largest value.

22. B
You can tell which calculation has the smallest value here just by looking at the numbers.
2.41 is the smallest left hand number in any of the calculations, and 0.06 is the smallest right hand number in any of the calculations.
Therefore, 2.41 × 0.06 (B) has the smallest value.

23. C
Use your knowledge of place value and multiplication to estimate the value of each calculation.
A: 52.7 can be rounded down to 50. It's being multiplied by eight tenths (0.8), so the answer will be around eight tenths of 50, which is 40 (50 ÷ 10 = 5. 5 × 8 = 40).
B: 0.527 is roughly one half (0.5). So the result of the calculation will be about half of 80 (around 40).
C: 5.27 can be rounded down to 5. The value of the calculation is around 5 × 800 = 4000.
D: 527 can be rounded down to 500. It's being multiplied by eight tenths (0.8), so the answer will be around eight tenths of 500, which is 400 (500 ÷ 10 = 50. 50 × 8 = 400).
E: 5270 can be rounded down to 5000. It's being multiplied by eight thousandths (0.008), so the answer will be around eight thousandths of 5000, which is 40 (5000 ÷ 1000 = 5. 5 × 8 = 40).
C has the largest value (around 4000).

24. E
Option A is based on the fact that 8 is one quarter of 32, so the answer must be one quarter of 7712, or 7712 ÷ 4.
Option B is based on the fact that 64 is double 32, so the answer must be double 7712, or 7712 × 2.
Option C is based on the fact that 16 is half of 32, so the answer must be half of 7712, or 7712 ÷ 2.
Option D is based on the fact that 241 × 33 will be one lot of 241 more than 7712, so 7712 + 241.
Option E should be 7712 ÷ 8 not 7712 ÷ 16 as 4 is one eighth of 32. E is incorrect.
Option F is based on he fact that 241 × 31 will be one lot of 241 less than 7712, so 7712 – 241.

25. E
Estimate the answer to each option.
A: 50 × 250 = 12 500
B: 5 × 2.5 = 12.5
C: 0.5 × 2.5 = 1.25
D: 50 × 25 = 1250
E: 5 × 25 = 125
From smallest to largest it would be C, B, E, D and A. So E would be in the middle.

26. D
Estimate the cost of each option.
A = 24 × 50p = £12
B = 6 × £2 = £12
C = 4 × £3 = £12
D = 2 × £5 = £10
E = £10 + (4 × 50p) = £12
So the cheapest option is D.

27. 286
Dave has 7 times as many stickers as Betty, so Dave has 7 × 26 = 182. Lorna has 3 times as many stickers as Betty, so Lorna has 3 × 26 = 78 stickers.
26 + 182 + 78 = 286 stickers.

28. 2000 kg
80 is double 40 and 25 kg is double 12.5 kg so you need to multiply 500 kg by 4.
4 × 500 kg = 2000 kg.

29. 4.86 kg
Mrs Greengrass is losing:
3 × 0.27 = 0.81 kg a week.
So after 6 weeks she will have lost 6 × 0.81 kg = 4.86 kg.

Page 9

You can do these divisions by partitioning the bigger number and dividing each of the parts by the other number. Alternatively, you could use short division. Which method you choose depends on the numbers you're working with.

1. 16
Break 96 into numbers that easily divide by 6. 96 breaks into 60 + 36. Divide these bits separately then add them together at the end.
60 ÷ 6 = 10, 36 ÷ 6 = 6, 10 + 6 = 16

2. 31
124 breaks into 100 + 24.
100 ÷ 4 = 25, 24 ÷ 4 = 6, 25 + 6 = 31

3. 144
720 breaks into 500 + 200 + 20.
500 ÷ 5 = 100, 200 ÷ 5 = 40, 20 ÷ 5 = 4,
100 + 40 + 4 = 144

4. 45
```
  0 4 5
7│3 3¹3 5
```

5. 107
```
  1 0 7
8│8 5 ⁵6
```

6. 22.4
```
  2 2 . 4
3│6 7 .¹2
```

7. remainder 2
```
  0 7 remainder 2
5│3 ³7
```

8. remainder 3
```
  0 2 5 remainder 3
4│1 ¹0²3
```

9. remainder 6
```
  0 1 5 remainder 6
8│1 ¹2 ⁴6
```

10. remainder 6
```
  0 2 0 remainder 6
9│1 ¹8 6
```

11. remainder 4
```
  0 3 0 remainder 4
8│2 ²4 4
```

12. remainder 1
```
  0 5 2 remainder 1
7│3 ³6 ¹5
```

13. 13
There are 81 + 10 = 91 children and staff altogether.
```
  1 3
7│9 ²1
```

14. 70 cm
```
  0 7 0
8│5 ⁵6 0
```

15. 18
```
  0 1 7 remainder 3
8│1 ¹3 ⁵9
```
3 are remaining, so Claire will need 1 more box, making a total of 18.

16. 33
```
  0 3 3 remainder 3
9│3 ³0 ³0
```
Mr Bond can set out 33 complete rows.

17. 97
```
  0 9 6 remainder 2
3│2 ²9 ²0
```
Two children are left over, so they will need an extra book to share between 2, so Mr Bond needs to hand out 97 song books in total.

18. B
Find the number that 128 divides by exactly.
```
  0 4 2 remainder 2
3│1 ¹2 8
  0 3 2
4│1 ¹2 8
```
It's divisible by 4 with no remainders.

Page 10

Use BODMAS to do each part of these calculations in the correct order.

1. 28
7 + 4 × 6 – 3 = 7 + 24 – 3 = 31 – 3 = 28

2. 9
6 + 8 ÷ 2 – 1 = 6 + 4 – 1 = 10 – 1 = 9

3. 3
7 + 6 – 5 × 2 = 7 + 6 – 10 = 13 – 10 = 3

4. 63
9 × 5 + 6 × 3 = 45 + 18 = 63

5. 18
3 × 5 + 15 ÷ 5 = 15 + 3 = 18

For questions 6-10, try the different signs until you find the one that works. Remember to use BODMAS to find the correct answer.

6. ×
6 + 4 is in brackets, so you know it must be done first: 7 _ (6 + 4) = 7 _ 10 = 70. 7 × 10 = 70

7. –
3 × 2 is in brackets, so you know it must be done first: 9 _ (3 × 2) = 9 _ 6 = 3, 9 – 6 = 3

8. +
8 × 1 is in brackets, so you know it must be done first: 3 _ (8 × 1)= 3 _ 8 = 11, 3 + 8 = 11

9. ÷
11 – 2 is in brackets, so you know it must be done first: 27 _ (11 – 2) = 27 _ 9 = 3. 27 ÷ 9 = 3.

10. ×
4 _ 5 is in brackets, so you know it must be done first. (This one's a bit trickier because you need to do the unknown calculation first.)
One more than (4 _ 5) is 21 from the equation. So (4 _ 5) must be 1 less than 21 = 20.
4 × 5 = 20.

11. –
9 _ 3 is in brackets, so you know it must be done first. Eleven more than (9 _ 3) is 17 from the equation. So (9 _ 3) must be 11 less than 17 = 6.
9 – 3 = 6.

12. C
Estimate to find the answer: 89 × 296 can be rounded to 90 × 300 = 27 000.
11 × 296 can be rounded to 10 × 300 = 3000.
27 000 + 3000 = 30 000. The only answer that's close to this is 29 600. Alternatively, you could add 89 and 11 together to get 100, then multiply this by 296.
100 × 296 = 29 600

13. D
A: 4 × 3 = 12, 7 + 6 – 12 = 13 – 12 = 1
B: 7 × 6 = 42, 42 – 4 = 38, 38 + 3 = 41
C: 4 × 3 = 12, 7 – 6 + 12 = 1 + 12 = 13
D: 7 × 6 = 42, 42 + 4 = 46, 46 – 3 = 43
E: 6 × 4 = 24, 7 + 24 – 3 = 31 – 3 = 28
F: 4 × 6 = 24, 24 + 7 – 3 = 31 – 3 = 28
So D is the answer.

14. – 40p
The price of each ticket has been rounded up by 5p. There are 8 tickets in total, 8 × 5 = 40.
So to complete the calculation you need to subtract 40p.

15. E
A: 10 ÷ 5 = 2, 60 – 20 + 2 = 40 + 2 = 42
B: 20 ÷ 10 = 2, 60 – 2 + 5 = 58 + 5 = 63
C: 10 ÷ 5 = 2, 60 + 20 – 2 = 80 – 2 = 78
D: 20 ÷ 10 = 2, 60 + 2 – 5 = 62 – 5 = 57
E: 60 ÷ 20 = 3, 3 + 10 – 5 = 13 – 5 = 8
E is the answer.

16. 2
To find 60 × 3.5 you can partition 3.5 into 3 + 0.5.
60 × 3 = 180, 60 × 0.5 = 30, 180 + 30 = 210.
This leaves you with 420 ÷ 210 = 2 as 420 is double 210.

Section Two
— Number Knowledge

Page 11

1. -3
The number which would be furthest to the left on a number line has the smallest value.

2. -2.1
The number which would be furthest to the left on a number line has the smallest value.

3. 3.4
The number which would be furthest to the right on a number line has the largest value.

4. 7.6
The number which would be furthest to the right on a number line has the largest value.

5. -1°C
The number which would be furthest to the right on a number line has the highest value.

6. <
-8 is less than 5.

7. <
-4 + 2 = -2, -2 is less than 2.

8. =
-2 + 6 = 4, 7 – 3 = 4, 4 is equal to 4.

9. >
-7 + 1 = -6, 5 – 13 = -8, -6 is greater than -8.

10. 30
2 + 4 + 6 + 8 + 10 = 30

11. 69
21 + 23 + 25 = 69

12. 1
The number has to be even, prime and less than 10. The only even prime number is 2.

13. 16
Both boys' ages are square numbers under 20. These are 1, 4, 9 and 16. Only 16 and 4 add up to 20. Feroz is older, so he must be 16.

14. 6
1 and 4 are square numbers. 2, 3 and 5 are prime numbers, 6 is neither square nor prime.

15. 25 °C
The highest temperature is 12 °C and the lowest is -13 °C. To get from -13 to 0 you add 13. To get from 0 to 12 you add 12.
13 + 12 = 25 °C

Pages 12-13

1. 1, 2, 4, 8, 16
16 divides exactly by 1, 2, 4, 8 and 16.

2. 1, 3, 5, 9, 15, 45
45 divides exactly by 1, 3, 5, 9, 15 and 45 and no other numbers.

3. 4
20 ÷ 4 = 5 and 32 ÷ 4 = 8

4. 12, 15, 16
3 × 4 = 12, 3 × 5 = 15, 4 × 4 = 16

5.   18
$18 \div 6 = 3, 18 \div 9 = 2$

6.   8
Factors of 16 = 1, 2, 4, 8, 16.
Factors of 24 = 1, 2, 3, 4, 6, 8, 12, 24.
Factors of 32 = 1, 2, 4, 8, 16, 32.
The highest number they all divide by is 8.

7.   8
Factors of 8 = 1, 2, 4, 8.
Factors of 16 = 1, 2, 4, 8, 16.
Factors of 32 = 1, 2, 4, 8, 16, 32.
The highest number they all divide by is 8.

8.   12
Factors of 60
= 1, 2, 3, 4, 5, 6, 10, 12, 15, 20, 30, 60.
Factors of 72
= 1, 2, 3, 4, 6, 8, 9, 12, 18, 24, 36, 72.
The highest number they both divide by is 12.

9.   32
Factors of 96
= 1, 2, 3, 4, 6, 8, 12, 16, 24, 32, 48, 96.
Factors of 128 = 1, 2, 4, 8, 16, 32, 64, 128.
The highest number they both divide by is 32.

10.   35
Multiples of 5 = 5, 10, 15, 20, 25, 30, 35...
Multiples of 7 = 7, 14, 21, 28, 35...
First multiple that is the same is 35.

11.   24
Multiples of 4 = 4, 8, 12, 16, 20, 24...
Multiples of 6 = 6, 12, 18, 24...
Multiples of 8 = 8, 16, 24...
First multiple that is the same is 24.

12.   12
Multiples of 2 = 2, 4, 6, 8, 10, 12...
Multiples of 6 = 6, 12...
Multiples of 12 = 12...
First multiple that is the same is 12.

13.   20
Multiples of 2 = 2, 4, 6, 8, 10, 12, 14, 16, 18, 20...
Multiples of 4 = 4, 8, 12, 16, 20...
Multiples of 5 = 5, 10, 15, 20...
First multiple that is the same is 20.

14.   3 × 5
$3 \times 5 = 15$. Both of these factors are already prime numbers.

15.   2 × 3 × 3
$3 \times 6 = 18$. 3 is a prime number so can be used as a prime factor. 6 can be written as 3×2, which are both prime numbers.

16.   2 × 2 × 3
$3 \times 4 = 12$. 3 is a prime number so can be used as a prime factor.
4 can be written as $2 \times 2 - 2$ is a prime number.

17.   2 × 2 × 3 × 3
$6 \times 6 = 36$. 6 can be written as 2×3, which are both prime numbers.

18.   100
The answer must be a multiple of 2 and 5. The first square number that is a multiple of 2 and 5 is 100.

19.   36
The answer must be a multiple of 3 and 6. The first square number that is a multiple of 3 and 6 is 36.

20.   18 seconds
The time in seconds until the kittens next miaow at the same time must be a multiple of 6 and 9. The lowest common multiple of 6 and 9 is 18. So the kittens will miaow at the same time again after 18 seconds.

21.   3 boxes
The cakes come in boxes of 4, so the total number of cakes must be a multiple of 4. There are 6 children who all get the same number, so the total number of cakes must also be a multiple of 6.
The lowest common multiple of 4 and 6 is 12.
3 boxes contain 12 cakes (3 × 4).

22.   45 cm
The distance in cm until the seeds next line up must be a multiple of 9 and a multiple of 15. The lowest common multiple of 15 and 9 is 45. So the seeds will line up again after 45 cm.

23.   90 cm
The distance in cm until all the seeds next line up must be a multiple of 9, 10 and 15. The lowest common multiple of 9, 10 and 15 is 90. So the seeds will line up again after 90 cm.

24.   8 friends
Factors of 56 = 1, 2, 4, 7, 8, 14, 28, 56.
Factors of 72
= 1, 2, 3, 4, 6, 8, 9, 12, 18, 24, 36, 72.
8 is the highest common factor — in order to give each friend in the group an equal number of sweets and an equal number of chocolate bars, the maximum number of people there can be in the group is 8.

25.   3
3 should be in the centre of the Venn diagram where all three circles overlap. 3 is a prime number, a multiple of 3 and a factor of 24.

26.   85
The factors of 64 are 1, 2, 4, 8, 16, 32 and 64.
The 4 square numbers in this list are
1, 4, 16 and 64. $1 + 4 + 16 + 64 = 85$

Page 14

To find a fraction of a number, divide the number by the denominator (bottom number) and multiply the result by the numerator (top number).

1.   6
$\frac{1}{2}$ of 12, $12 \div 2 = 6$

2.   3
$\frac{1}{3}$ of 9, $9 \div 3 = 3$

3.   2
$\frac{2}{8}$ of 8, $8 \div 8 = 1, 1 \times 2 = 2$

4.   8
$\frac{2}{6}$ of 24, $24 \div 6 = 4, 4 \times 2 = 8$

5.   27
$\frac{3}{4}$ of 36, $36 \div 4 = 9, 9 \times 3 = 27$

6.   36
$\frac{4}{5}$ of 45, $45 \div 5 = 9, 9 \times 4 = 36$

7. $\frac{1}{3}$ of 27
$\frac{1}{4}$ of 32. $32 \div 4 = 8, 8 \times 1 = 8$
$\frac{1}{3}$ of 27. $27 \div 3 = 9, 9 \times 1 = 9$

8. $\frac{2}{3}$ of 33
$\frac{2}{3}$ of 33. $33 \div 3 = 11, 11 \times 2 = 22$
$\frac{1}{5}$ of 100. $100 \div 5 = 20, 20 \times 1 = 20$

9. $\frac{2}{5}$ of 25
$\frac{2}{5}$ of 25. $25 \div 5 = 5, 5 \times 2 = 10$
$\frac{1}{2}$ of 18. $18 \div 2 = 9, 9 \times 1 = 9$

10. $\frac{4}{5}$ of 35
$\frac{4}{5}$ of 35. $35 \div 5 = 7, 7 \times 4 = 28$
$\frac{5}{6}$ of 30. $30 \div 6 = 5, 5 \times 5 = 25$

11. $\frac{7}{8}$ of 48
$\frac{1}{3}$ of 120. $120 \div 3 = 40, 40 \times 1 = 40$
$\frac{7}{8}$ of 48. $48 \div 8 = 6, 6 \times 7 = 42$

12. $\frac{7}{9}$ of 72
$\frac{6}{11}$ of 88. $88 \div 11 = 8, 8 \times 6 = 48$
$\frac{7}{9}$ of 72. $72 \div 9 = 8, 8 \times 7 = 56$

13.   B
8 apples divided between 12 children would give $\frac{8}{12}$ of an apple for each child. This fraction can be simplified to $\frac{2}{3}$ if you divide the numerator and the denominator by 4.

14.   A
6 out of the 16 squares are shaded, giving the fraction $\frac{6}{16}$. This can be simplified to $\frac{3}{8}$ if you divide the numerator and the denominator by 2.

15.   £2.60
First work out $\frac{1}{5}$ of £4.50: £4.50 ÷ 5 = £0.90 — this is how much Josh gives to his sister.
Next work out $\frac{2}{9}$ of £4.50:
£4.50 ÷ 9 = £0.50, £0.50 × 2 = £1.00 — this is how much Josh gives to his friend.
Add the two amounts and subtract them from £4.50 to work out what is left:
£0.90 + £1.00 = £1.90
£4.50 − £1.90 = £2.60

16.   20 marbles
Martha had 12 marbles after giving $\frac{2}{5}$ to Joseph, so 12 is $\frac{3}{5}$ of the total number of marbles.
If $\frac{3}{5}$ = 12, then $\frac{1}{5}$ = 12 ÷ 3 = 4.
So the total number of marbles she started with = 4 × 5 = 20

17.   £0.20
Dog Empire — 2 chews would cost
£1 + £0.50 = £1.50.
So 4 chews would cost £1.50 + £1.50 = £3.
Dog Shop — before a discount, 4 chews would cost 4 × £1.20 = £4.80.
As Aarti is buying at least 3, she gets $\frac{1}{3}$ off:
$\frac{1}{3}$ of £4.80 is £4.80 ÷ 3 = £1.60.
So the price of 4 chews is £4.80 − £1.60 = £3.20.
The difference in price is £3.20 − £3 = £0.20

Page 15

1.   1:3
There are 3 red apples for every 9 green apples, which gives a ratio of 3:9. The question asks for the ratio to be written in its simplest form, so divide both parts of the ratio by the same number.
3 and 9 are both divisible by 3 giving 1:3, which can't be simplified any more.

2.   15 g
Gabriel adds 5 g of ginger, so 5 g = 1 part.
He needs to add 3 parts cinnamon so multiply the quantity of ginger by 3: 5 g × 3 = 15 g

3.   7.5 g
Lara adds 22.5 g of cinnamon, so 22.5 g = 3 parts.
She needs to add 1 part ginger so divide the quantity of cinnamon by 3. 22.5 g ÷ 3 = 7.5 g

4.   3:1
The pie chart can be split into quarters.
$\frac{3}{4}$ is occupied by frogs and $\frac{1}{4}$ by newts.
That means that for every 3 frogs, there is 1 newt, which can be written in the ratio 3:1.

5.   8 robins
Nick expects that 1 in every 4 birds will be a robin. This is another way of saying $\frac{1}{4}$ of the birds will be robins. If he sees 32 birds in total, $\frac{1}{4}$ will be robins, so 32 ÷ 4 = 8.

6.   3 black rabbits
2 out of every 3 is the same as $\frac{2}{3}$.
So $\frac{2}{3}$ of Melissa's rabbits are ginger, and $\frac{1}{3}$ must be black. 6 ginger rabbits make up $\frac{2}{3}$ of her rabbits.
To work out how many rabbits make up $\frac{1}{3}$, divide by 2: 6 ÷ 2 = 3, so she has 3 black rabbits.

7.   16 games
The ratio of racing games to football games is 3:5. He owns 6 racing games, which is 6 ÷ 3 = 2 times as many as in the ratio. Multiply the number of football games in the ratio (5) by 2 to find out how many football games he owns 5 × 2 = 10
So he owns 6 racing games and 10 football games, which is 6 + 10 = 16 games in total.

8.   300:200
Add the numbers in the ratio together: 3 + 2 = 5
500 ÷ 5 = 100. So one part equals 100.
100 × 3 = 300 and 100 × 2 = 200 so 500 is 300:200 in the ratio 3:2.

9. 240:180

Add the numbers in the ratio together: 4 + 3 = 7
Divide 420 by this to find what one part of the ratio equals: 420 ÷ 7 = 60.
60 × 4 = 240 and 60 × 3 = 180 so 420 is 240:180 when divided in the ratio 4:3.

10. 400:240

Add the numbers in the ratio together: 5 + 3 = 8
Divide 640 by this to find what one part of the ratio equals: 640 ÷ 8 = 80
80 × 5 = 400 and 80 × 3 = 240 so 640 is 400:240 when divided in the ratio 5:3.

11. £40

Find out how much each charity gets:
5 + 4 + 3 = 12. £240 ÷ 12 = £20.
One part is worth £20, so the money is split in the ratio (5 × 20):(4 × 20):(3 × 20) = 100:80:60.
Then work out the difference between the largest and smallest amounts: £100 – £60 = £40.

Page 16

1. $^{29}/_{100}$

29% means '29 out of 100' (which can't be simplified).

2. 0.15

To convert the fraction into a decimal, you need to make the denominator equal to 100, multiply numerator and denominator by 5 here:
$^3/_{20} = ^{15}/_{100}$.
Then divide the numerator by 100 to convert to a decimal: 15 ÷ 100 = 0.15

3. 62%

$^{31}/_{50}$ is equivalent to $^{62}/_{100}$ (multiply the numerator and denominator by 2). $^{62}/_{100}$ is 62%.

4. $^{23}/_{50}$

46% means '46 out of 100'. So that's $^{46}/_{100}$.
This can be simplified to $^{23}/_{50}$ by dividing the numerator and the denominator by 2.

5. 23

This question is asking you to find 46% of 50.
50 ÷ 100 = 0.5, 0.5 × 46 = 23.
So 23 of Ed's friends have dogs.

6. 7

To find 10% of 70 you can divide 70 by 10, so 10% of 70 is 70 ÷ 10 = 7

7. 3

25% of 12 is the same as $^1/_4$ of 12. 12 ÷ 4 = 3

8. 128

1% of 6400 is 6400 ÷ 100 = 64,
2% is 64 × 2 = 128

9. 24

To find 10% of 80 you can divide 80 by 10, so 10% of 80 is 80 ÷ 10 = 8, 30% is 8 × 3 = 24

10. 60%

There are five triangles, so each triangle is 100 ÷ 5 = 20% of the shape.
Three triangles are not shaded, so this is 3 × 20% = 60% of the shape.
Alternatively, 3 out of the 5 triangles aren't shaded, so that's $^3/_5$. This is equivalent to $^{60}/_{100}$ (multiply the numerator and denominator by 20).
$^{60}/_{100}$ = 60%.

11. £8.40

10% of £10.50 is £10.50 ÷ 10 = £1.05
So, 20% = £1.05 × 2 = £2.10
£10.50 – £2.10 = £8.40

12. 13

Find the total of red and yellow rose bushes.
40% are red. 10% is 30 ÷ 10 = 3.
So 40% = 4 × 3 = 12 red rose bushes.
$^1/_6$ are yellow. 30 ÷ 6 = 5 yellow rose bushes.
So 30 – 12 – 5 = 13 white rose bushes.

13. 40%

Add up the total number of pupils.
10 + 4 + 12 + 4 = 30. 12 out of 30 take the bus, so $^{12}/_{30}$ — you can simplify this to $^4/_{10}$ by dividing the numerator and the denominator by 3.
$^4/_{10}$ is equivalent to $^{40}/_{100}$ — so that's 40%.

Section Three — Number Problems

Pages 17-18

Replace a with 6 in each calculation.

1. 11

6 + 5 = 11

2. 24

4 × 6 = 24

3. 9

(2 × 6) – 3 = 12 – 3 = 9

4. 30

(3 × 6) + (2 × 6) = 18 + 12 = 30

5. 50

5(6 + 4) = 5 × 10 = 50

6. 2a

2 lots of a = 2 × a, or 2a.

7. 3△ – 2

3 × △ = 3△, 3△ – 2

8. 4x + 3x

5x + 2x = 7x, and 4x + 3x = 7x

9. 6a + 3b

3(2a + b) means:
(2a + b) + (2a + b) + (2a + b) = 6a + 3b.

10. 2☆ – 2(☆ + 0)

2(☆ + 0) means (☆ + 0) + (☆ + 0), which is 2☆.
So the expression is the same as 2☆ – 2☆.

11. 9

4 × 7 = 28. Whatever x represents, the product of 3 and x must be smaller than 28. The biggest number x could be is 9. 3 × 9 = 27.

12. A

Substituting values of f = 3 and r = 12 into the four equations gives the results:
Shine o' Grime: 50 + 12 + 3 = £65
Wishy Washy: (5 × 12) + (6 × 3) = £78
The Sud Buds: 2 × 12 × 3 = £72
Top Mopz: 30 + 12 × 3 = £66

13. £39

Claire has 9 rooms and 1 floor.
This gives a result of 30 + 9 × 1 = £39.

14. 16

Rosemary has a two-storey house meaning f = 2.
Using the given equation, £92 = 5r + 6 × 2.
This can be simplified to 92 = 5r + 12, leading to 80 = 5r. This means that r, the number of rooms = 80 ÷ 5 = 16

15. £28

From question 14, we know Rosemary has 2 floors and 16 rooms. Substituting this into the equation for The Sud Buds gives 2 × 16 × 2 = £64.
Wishy Washy cost her £92, meaning a saving of 92 – 64 = £28.

16. £525

d = 9, so cost = 75 + (50 × 9) = 75 + 450 = £525

17. E

Each passenger, or n, costs £5.
So that can be shown as 5 × n, or 5n.
The total cost is 5n plus £260 = 260 + 5n

18. £69

Put m = 25 into the formula.
15 + 2(25 + 2) = 15 + 2 × 27 = 15 + 54 = £69

19. A

Each game, or n, costs £35.
So that can be shown as 35 × n, or 35n.
The total cost is 35n plus the cost of the console = 150 + 35n.

20. 100 minutes

If ⊕ = 8, then time = 60 + (5 × 8) = 60 + 40 = 100 minutes.

21. C

3 pieces, each x cm long, are 3x cm long in total.
The plank was 400 cm long, so after the three pieces are cut off it is (400 – 3x) cm long.

22. 130 cm

If x = 90, 3x = 90 × 3
The plank has length 400 – (90 × 3) = 130 cm

23. A

Two shelves of length a equals two lots of a, or 2a.
One shelf of length b and one shelf of length c is equal to b + c.
Therefore the equation is 150 = 2a + b + c.

24. a = 33, c = 54

If b = 30, then substituting into the equation gives 150 = 2a + 30 + c.
This gives 150 – 30 = 120 = 2a + c.
If c is known to be (a + 21), the equation is equal to 120 = 2a + a + 21. This can be simplified to 120 – 21 = 2a + a so 99 = 3a.
Solving 99 = 3a gives 99 ÷ 3 = a, so a = 33.
c is found by substituting a = 33 into c = a + 21:
c = 33 + 21 = 54

Pages 19-20

To find the rule in a sequence, try to find how to get from one number to another. It can help to look at the difference between the numbers, or try to spot a pattern, e.g. the numbers double each time.

1. 21

The rule of the sequence is add 3.
So the missing term = 18 + 3 = 21

2. 101

The rule of the sequence is subtract 3.
So the missing term = 104 – 3 = 101

3. 16

The rule of the sequence is subtract 5.
So the missing term = 21 – 5 = 16

4. 2

The rule of the sequence is add 0.25.
So the missing term = 1.75 + 0.25 = 2

5. 4

The rule of the sequence is double the previous number. So the missing term must be half of the following term, 8 ÷ 2 = 4

6. 22

The sequence is 6, 10, 14, 18, 22...

7. 10

The sequence is 30, 25, 20, 15, 10...

8. 48

The sequence is 3, 6, 12, 24, 48...

9. 11

The sequence is 23, 20, 17, 14, 11...

10. 7

The sequence is 5, 5.5, 6, 6.5, 7...

11. D

Choose a term and test each expression to find out which gives the correct value.
E.g. for the second term, n = 2: substitute 2 for n in each expression and see which gives the correct value, 7. Only 4n – 1 gives 7 when n = 2: (4 × 2) – 1 = 7.
If there had been more than one expression which gave the correct value, you would have had to choose a different term and test which one of the expressions was correct.

6

12. B

When n = even, even × 4 = even.
Even − 1 = odd.
When n = odd, odd × 4 = even.
Even − 1 = odd.

13. 2.5, 3.75

For the second term in the sequence, n = 2.
Using $\frac{n}{4} + n$, $\frac{2}{4} + 2 = 2.5$
For the third term in the sequence, n = 3.
Using $\frac{n}{4} + n$, $\frac{3}{4} + 3 = 3.75$

14. 25

When n = 20, $\frac{n}{4} + n$ is equal to $\frac{20}{4} + 20 = 25$.

15. D

Use the equation $\frac{n}{4} + n = 50$ and solve for n.
Multiplying everything by 4 gives n + 4n = 200 so
5n = 200 and n = 200 ÷ 5 = 40
Alternatively, you could try putting in each option
as the value of n until you find the one that gives
$\frac{n}{4} + n = 50$.

16. 21

There are 6 sticks in the first shape, 11 in the
second shape, and 16 in the third shape. So each
shape has 5 sticks more than the shape before.
The next shape will be made of 16 + 5 = 21 sticks.

17. 22

There are 4 sticks in the first shape, 10 in the
second shape, and 16 in the third shape. So each
shape has 6 sticks more than the shape before.
The next shape will be made of 16 + 6 = 22 sticks.

18. 10

Continuing the sequence, 20 − 15 = 5, so 5 is the
sixth number. The seventh number is the difference
between the 5th and the 6th numbers.
15 − 5 = 10. 10 is the seventh number.

19. 37

Tom's sequence is 73, 64, 55, 46, 37...
Mark's sequence is 25, 29, 33, 37...

20. -0.25

Nadiah's sequence is: 6, 4.75, 3.5, 2.25, 1, -0.25...

21. 22, 67, 202

Bria's sequence is 2, 7, 22, 67, 202...

22. 36

The expression for the sequence is $\frac{1}{2}n(n + 1)$, so
substitute 8 into the expression and follow the
rules of BODMAS.
$\frac{1}{2} × 8(8 + 1) = \frac{1}{2} × 8 × 9 = 4 × 9 = 36$

23. 6

The number of marbles increases by 2 in each shape.
Shape 4 has 10 marbles, so shape 5 will have
10 + 2 = 12 marbles.
Shape 6 will have 12 + 2 = 14 marbles and shape 7
will have 14 + 2 = 16 marbles.
Fatima has 15 marbles so the highest term she can
make is the 6th term.

Pages 21-22

1. £80

Matt worked for 3 hours + 4 hours + 3 hours, so
that's 10 hours in total. 10 × £8 = £80

2. £2

If one shirt costs £11, then two shirts would be
2 × £11 = £22.
£24 − £22 = £2, which is the cost of the tie.

3. 4

Half of 56 is 28 (56 ÷ 2 = 28). Finlay eats 8
chocolates per day.
Day 1: 56 − 8 = 48 left.
Day 2: 48 − 8 = 40 left.
Day 3: 40 − 8 = 32 left,
Day 4: 32 − 8 = 24 left, which is less than half.

4. 81

The only number which is a multiple of 9 is 81
(9 × 9 = 81).

5. 78

5 litres marked out 130 spaces, so
1 litre could mark out 130 ÷ 5 = 26 spaces.
Multiply by 3 to find how many spaces 3 litres could
mark out 26 × 3 = 78

6. C

Find the total price for each answer option
until you find the correct answer.
C: 1 calculator + 1 ruler + 1 rubber
= £4.50 + £1.00 + 75p = £6.25

7. 450 g

Find the weight of one ball: 750 g ÷ 5 = 150 g.
Two balls are used, that's 150 g × 2 = 300 g,
which leaves 750 g − 300 g = 450 g.

8. 0.8 kg

6 people need 1.2 kg, so 1 person needs
1.2 kg ÷ 6 = 0.2 kg.
4 people would need 4 × 0.2 = 0.8 kg.

9. £36.25

2 shirts = 2 × £12.50 = £25
Boots = £32
3 pairs of socks = 3 × £2.25 = £6.75
£25 + £32 + £6.75 = £63.75
£100 − £63.75 = £36.25

10. £1.25

At their normal price, 5 pairs of socks would sell for
5 × £2.25 = £11.25.
In the sale they sell for £10.
There is a saving of £11.25 − £10 = £1.25

11. £39.20

The usual cost of two pairs of shorts is
2 × £8.50 = £17.
The usual price of football boots is £32.
Together this costs £17 + £32 = £49.
10% of £49 is 49 ÷ 10 = £4.90.
20% is £4.90 × 2 = £9.80.
The sale price is £49 − £9.80 = £39.20

12. £1.15

If Connor received 10p change from £7, he spent
£6.90. (£7 − £6.90 = 10p.)
1 choc ice costs £6.90 ÷ 6 = £1.15

13. D

He spends 24p. If 1 snake costs 4p, then 24p buys
24 ÷ 4 = 6 snakes.
2¾ g is the same as 2.75 g, so 6 snakes would
weigh 6 × 2.75 g = 16.5 g.

14. E

A: This can be true, e.g. Chris could have sold
29 teas and 28 coffees.
B: This can be true, e.g. people could have bought
29 coffees and 28 teas.
C: This can be true, e.g. Chris could have sold
31 teas and 26 coffees.
D: This can be true, e.g. Chris could have sold
38 coffees and 19 teas.
E: This cannot be true. The total number of teas and
coffees sold is odd (57), so the sum of the number
of teas and coffees sold must be an odd number
added to an even number.
The difference between an odd number and an even
number is always odd. 10 is an even number, so this
cannot be true.

15. 170 cm

There are 10 rows of bricks. There will be
10 concrete layers altogether — 9 between the
rows plus one beneath the bottom row.
Total height of bricks = 15 × 10 = 150 cm.
Total height of concrete layers: 2 × 10 = 20 cm.
So the total height of the wall is:
150 + 20 = 170 cm.

16. 4 litres

A 2 litre bottle can make 6 × 800 ml of squash.
6 × 800 ml = 4800 ml.
The total volume of squash needed is 48 × 200 ml.
48 × 200 ml = 9600 ml. 9600 ml is double
4800 ml, so the amount of concentrate needed is
2 × 2 litres = 4 litres.

17. £96

The children spent 24p on soap and wax for each
car, so in total they spent 24p × 100 = £24. The
total amount charged is £1.20 × 100 = £120.
The amount they raised for charity is the total
amount charged, minus the total amount spent on
soap and wax. £120 − £24 = £96.
Alternatively, you could work out the profit on each
car wash, which would be the amount charged, minus
the cost of the soap and wax, £1.20 − 24p = 96p.
Now multiply this by the number of cars washed,
96p × 100 = £96

18. £1.98

The ingredients shown are enough for 24 rock cakes
and Ben wants to make 36.
36 ÷ 24 = 1.5, so you need to multiply the amount
of each ingredient in the recipe by 1.5.
There are 2 eggs in the recipe, so 2 × 1.5 = 3 eggs.
3 × 22p = 66p. The ingredients shown are enough
for 20 lemon buns, and Ben wants to make 60.
60 ÷ 20 = 3, so you need to multiply the amount of
each ingredient in the recipe by 3.
There are 2 eggs in the recipe, so 2 × 3 = 6 eggs.
6 × 22p = £1.32. £1.32 + 66p = £1.98

19. £14.70

If 24 rock cakes cost £5.04, one rock cake costs:

$$24 \overline{\smash{)}5{.}^{5}0^{2}4} \quad £0.2\,1$$

To make 70 rock cakes, it would cost £0.21 × 70
= £14.70

20. 68

If each bun costs 20p to make and sells at 50p,
there's a profit per cake of 50 − 20 = 30p.
To make £20.40, Ben must have sold
20.40 ÷ 0.30 lemon buns.
This is equal to 204 ÷ 3 = 68 lemon buns.

Section Four
— Data Handling

Page 23

For questions 1 and 2 you need to read the values
from the table.

1. 8

2. 5

3. 8

17 pupils in Class C use a car to get to school and 9
catch the bus. 17 − 9 = 8 pupils.

4. Class A

15 pupils in Class A catch the bus, compared to 14
in Class B and 9 in Class C.

5. 75

Add all the entries in the bus and car columns.
15 + 14 + 9 + 8 + 12 + 17 = 75 pupils.

6. Class C

17 pupils in Class C use a car to get to school,
compared to 12 in Class B and 8 in Class A.

7. 37

Add the entire row for Class B.
14 + 12 + 5 + 6 = 37 pupils.

8. 8

The values in the table must add up to 40 (the
number of children asked). So add up the numbers
given and subtract this from 40 to find the missing
number: 8 + 4 + 8 + 5 + 7 = 32. 40 − 32 = 8

9. 27

Add together the number of children who receive
less than £1 and the number who receive between
£1 and £3.50: 15 + 12 = 27

10.

	Large	Small	Total
Pepperoni	6	**2**	8
Cheese and Ham	**9**	7	**16**
Total	**15**	9	24

The numbers in the last row must show the totals for each column. The numbers in the last column must show the totals for each row.
Since 8 pepperoni pizzas were ordered, and 6 of them were large, the number of small pepperoni pizzas ordered must be 8 – 6 = 2.
Since 24 pizzas were ordered in total, the number of cheese and ham pizzas must be 24 – 8 = 16.
The number of large pizzas ordered is equal to number of pizzas ordered – number of small pizzas ordered. This is 24 – 9 = 15.
You can use the number of large pizzas or the number of cheese and ham pizzas to find the number of large cheese and ham pizzas:
15 – 6 = 9 or 16 – 7 = 9

Pages 24-25

1.   3
Read the value off the graph. The total number for a category is in line with the top of the category bar.

2.   F
Only one person said fish were their favourite pet. This is option F.

3.   1
6 people preferred cats. 5 people preferred hamsters. 6 – 5 = 1

4.   6
7 people preferred dogs. Only one person said that fish were their favourite pet. 7 – 1 = 6.

5.   27
Add the total values from all categories.
5 + 6 + 7 + 3 + 5 + 1 = 27.

6.   A and E
Both horses and hamsters were the favourite pet of 5 people.

7.   45
Each picture represents 20 fish.
There are 2¼ pictures.
¼ of a picture represents 20 ÷ 4 = 5 fish.
So 2¼ pictures represents 20 + 20 + 5 = 45 fish.

8.   75
The bar chart shows that 375 people watched the 7 pm film on Friday. There are 450 seats available so the number of empty seats is 450 – 375 = 75

9.   13
Each symbol = 4 drinks.
There are 4¾ symbols for blackcurrant drinks.
4 × 4 = 16 drinks. ¾ of 4 = 3 drinks. So the total number of blackcurrant drinks is 16 + 3 = 19.
Cherryade is represented by 1½ symbols.
4 × 1 = 4, ½ of 4 = 2. So the total number of cherryade drinks is 4 + 2 = 6. So the difference between the number of blackcurrant and cherryade drinks is 19 – 6 = 13 drinks.
Alternatively, you could find the difference in the number of symbols for blackcurrant and cherryade drinks, then multiply this by 4:
4¾ – 1½ = 3¼ symbols. 4 × 3 = 12, ¼ of 4 = 1.
So the difference in the number of drinks is 12 + 1 = 13 drinks

10.   D
18 teenagers preferred to spend their pocket money on technology and this represents ¼ of the pie chart (as this section is 90° which is ¼ of the whole 360° pie chart).
Multiply 18 by 4 to find the total number of teenagers in the survey. 18 × 4 = 72

11.   4 minutes
The flat portion of the graph between 11 and 15 minutes shows that Joe is not moving. This must be when he stopped to talk to his friend.
15 – 11 = 4 minutes

12.   10 minutes
Joe's walk is 2000 m in total. The halfway point of his walk is 2000 ÷ 2 = 1000 m. The point at which Joe reaches 1000 m can be read off the graph.

13.   750
The shot put section has an angle of 60° and represents 250 tickets. The high jump section covers half of the pie chart. As the total of the angles in a pie chart is 360°, the size of the high jump angle is 180° (360° ÷ 2).
The size of the high jump section is three times the size of the shot put section (60° × 3 = 180°) so the high jump sold three times as many tickets.
3 × 250 = 750 tickets

14.   500
The angle that corresponds to javelin can be calculated as 180° – 60° = 120°. If shot put sold 250 tickets at 60°, then 120° sells 250 × 2 = 500 tickets.

15. $4.50
Pounds are written on the x-axis. Find £3 on this axis. If you travel from this point vertically up to the line, and then horizontally across to the y-axis, the corresponding value in $ can be read off.

16.   £4
Dollars are written on the y-axis. Find $6 on this axis. If you travel from this point horizontally across to the line, and then vertically down to the x-axis, the corresponding value in £ can be read off.

17.   £30
The graph tells you that $4.50 equals £3. $45 is ten times greater than $4.50, so multiply £3 by ten to find the number of pounds. £3 × 10 = £30

Page 26

The mode is the most common number in a group. For questions 1-6, you need to find the number that occurs most often in each set.

1.   6
2.   19
3.   18
4.   3
5.   19
6.   40

The median is the middle value in a group. To answer questions 7-12, you need to arrange the values from smallest to biggest, and find the middle value in each row.
If there is an even number of values, then find the number halfway between the two middle values.

7.   12
8.   18
9.   8
10.   58
11.   27.5
12.   14.5

13.   2
To calculate the mean, add up all the numbers of goals: (0 + 2 + 4 + 2 + 5 + 1 + 0 + 2 = 16) then divide by the number of matches they played (8).
16 ÷ 8 = 2

14.   Tuesday
The range is the difference between the highest and lowest temperature. The range on Tuesday is 14 – 6 = 8 °C. This is larger than any other day.

15.   14 °C
From the table, highs of 14 °C appear twice in the week. All other temperatures appear only once.

16.   4 °C
Add all the lows together and find the mean:
12 + 6 + 4 – 3 – 1 + 4 + 6 = 28.
There are 7 bits of data so 28 ÷ 7 = 4 °C

17.   4 °C
List the data in numerically ascending order:
-3, -1, 4, 4, 6, 6, 12
The middle value is 4.

18.   10
Mean = total score of the six tests ÷ number of tests (6). So, to work out the total score of the six tests, multiply the mean by 6:
7 × 6 = 42. To find the missing score, subtract the other scores from 42.
42 – 4 – 6 – 7 – 10 – 5 = 10.

Page 27

1.   A
Jamie got 25%, Hasim got 10% and Ted got 5%. Lex didn't get any votes, so he got 0%. Despite only having 12 votes, Anne received a higher percentage than Jamie, Hasim, Ted and Lex. So that leaves Anne with 100% – 25% – 10% – 5% = 60% (There were only twenty voters).

2.   C
The pictures in this pictogram are different sizes and this is misleading. For example the crocodile row appears longer than the snake row, but there are only 3 × 4 = 12 crocodiles compared to 5.5 × 4 = 22 snakes

3.   D
The steps on the vertical axis double each time. What the graph appears to show at a glance is different to what the data actually shows. For example, the number of calls on Wednesday is actually double the number on Tuesday, but the difference between the values plotted on the graph looks smaller than this.

4.   D
The number of children with blue eyes is ¾ of the number with green eyes. There are 24 children with blue eyes and 32 with green eyes.
¼ of 32 is 32 ÷ 4 = 8 so ¾ of 32 = 3 × 8 = 24. (The blue bar is not ¾ of the height of the green bar because the scale does not start at zero.)

Page 28

1.   ³⁄₈
Three of the eight sections contain the number 4 so the probability is ³⁄₈.

2.   ⁵⁄₈
Five of the sections contain an odd number so the probability is ⁵⁄₈.

3.   0
The number 7 isn't on the spinner, so there's no chance of it landing on 7.

4.   C
The number 5 only occurs in one section. This is less than the other numbers (3 and 4), so spinning a 5 is least likely.

5.   3
Four of the eight sections contain a 3, so the probability of spinning a 3 is ⁴⁄₈ or ½ = 50%.

6.   ³⁄₆ or ½
Three out of the six numbers on a dice are even, so the probability of rolling an even number is ³⁄₆ or ½.

7.   ⁵⁄₁₂
Five of the 12 marbles are red so the probability of picking a red marble is ⁵⁄₁₂.

8.   ⁷⁄₁₂
Seven of the 12 marbles are green so the probability of picking a green marble is ⁷⁄₁₂.

9. $\frac{3}{9}$ or $\frac{1}{3}$

Three of the nine socks are striped, so the probability of picking a striped sock is $\frac{3}{9} = \frac{1}{3}$.

10. $\frac{6}{11}$

There are 11 letters in the word so 11 possible outcomes.
There are 2Ms, 2As and 1S (5 tiles) so only the remaining 6 tiles (11 – 5 = 6) will give a letter that is not M, S, or A. So the probability is $\frac{6}{11}$.

11. 7

One quarter of the scarves are yellow so the number of yellow scarves = 16 ÷ 4 = 4.
You know that 5 scarves are green so the rest are red. 16 – 4 – 5 = 7

12. B

There are 16 jars of jam (6 + 3 + 4 + 3 = 16) and 4 of them are strawberry. So the probability of picking strawberry is $\frac{4}{16}$ or $\frac{1}{4}$.

13. $\frac{4}{22}$ or $\frac{2}{11}$

At the start $\frac{1}{4}$ of the sweets in the bag are bears (24 ÷ 4 = 6). After 2 bears are removed this leaves a total of 22 sweets of which 4 are bears. This means the probability of choosing a bear next is $\frac{4}{22} = \frac{2}{11}$.

Section Five
— Shape and Space

Page 29

1. 40°

The three angles in a triangle add up to 180°.
Angle x = 180° – 65° – 75° = 40°.

2. 105°

Angles on a straight line add up to 180°.
Angle y = 180° – 75° = 105°

3. 295°

Angles around a point add up to 360°.
Angle z = 360° – 65° = 295°

4. 180°

Angles on a straight line add up to 180°

5. 123°

Angles on a straight line add up to 180°.
Angle U = 180° – 34° – 23° = 123°

6. 23°

The three angles in a triangle add up to 180°.
180° – 90° – 67° = 23°

7. B

The angle looks to be half of the size of a right angle. A right angle is 90°, so the size of the angle is about 90° ÷ 2 = 45°

8. A

An obtuse angle is an angle that is bigger than 90° and smaller than 180°. Shape A contains two obtuse angles.

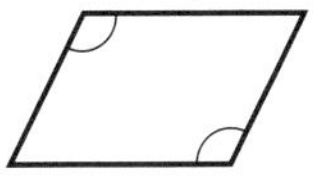

9. 210°

Each angle in an equilateral triangle is 60° and each angle in a square is a right angle (90°). The shaded angle is made up of one angle from the square and two angles from the equilateral triangles:
90° + 60° + 60° = 210°

10. 10

There are 360° in a full circle and the numbers on a clock face divide the circle into 12 equal sectors. Each sector has an angle of 360° ÷ 12 = 30°. The minute hand has moved 300° so it has moved through 10 sectors (30° x 10 = 300°). If the minute hand moves on 10 sectors from 12 it is pointing at 10.

11. 70°

The angles in a quadrilateral add up to 360°. The size of the fourth angle inside the shape = 360° – 85° – 83° – 82° = 110° The angles on a straight line add up to 180° so angle y = 180° – 110° = 70°

12. 240°

You need to use your answer to the previous question to work this out. You know that angle y = 70°, so you can now work out the missing angle in the triangle.
180° – 70° – 73° = 37°. There are 360° in a full circle so angle z = 360° – 37° – 83° = 240°

Pages 30-31

1. C

Shape C is the only shape with exactly two right angles.

2. D

An isosceles triangle has three sides in total, with two that are equal in length — D is the only shape with three sides and two that are equal in length.

3. C

A pentagon has five sides — C is the only shape with five sides.

4. H

A quadrilateral has four sides. H is a quadrilateral with four sides that are equal in length.

5. B

The two horizontal lines in B are parallel and the shape has no right angles.

6. E

A trapezium has one pair of parallel sides.

7. B

The internal angle of a regular polygon increases as the number of sides increases. An octagon has 8 sides which is more than the other shapes given.

8. D

Perpendicular sides are at right angles to each other (see the diagram).

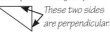 *These two sides are perpendicular.*

9. BC

Parallel lines have the same slope so BC is parallel to DE.

10. AB

ABE is an isosceles triangle so AB is equal in length to AE.

11. A

The points form a quadrilateral with two pairs of non-parallel sides of equal length (AE = AB and EF = BF), and a pair of opposite obtuse angles that are equal (at points B and E), so the shape formed is a kite.

12. C

Joining points BCDEF makes a shape with five sides. A pentagon is the name given to a shape with five sides.

13. D

Shape D is a hexagon so it cannot be placed in either the triangle or quadrilateral rows of the table.

14. 60°

The angles of any quadrilateral add up to 360°. The obtuse angles in a kite are equal, so angle x = 360° – (125° + 125° + 50°) = 60°

15. C

The diagram below shows the reflected isosceles triangle which has 2 equal sides. It is a rhombus because it has 4 equal sides, 2 equal obtuse angles and 2 equal acute angles.

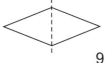

16. 450 mm

The radius of a circle is half of the diameter: 900 ÷ 2 = 450 mm

17. C

Pentagons do not fit together without gaps whereas the other 4 shapes do. For example:

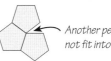 *Another pentagon could not fit into this space.*

18. 150°

The marked angles inside the rhombus are both 30° so the total of the unknown angles must be 360° – 30° – 30° = 300° Opposite angles in a rhombus are equal so angle a must be 300° ÷ 2 = 150°

19. E

A rectangle, rhombus, trapezium and square all have parallel sides whereas a kite does not.

20. 130°

The acute angles in a parallelogram are equal. Each acute angle = 90 – 40 = 50°. The sum of the two obtuse angles is 360 – (50+ 50) = 260°. So the size of each obtuse angle = 260 ÷ 2 = 130°.

Pages 32-33

1. C and D

Count the number of squares in each shape to find its area.
The area of shape C = 10 squares + 4 half squares = 12 squares.
The area of shape D is also 12 squares.

For questions 2-4, work out the perimeter of each shape by adding the lengths of each side together. In question 2, shape S is a rectangle, so the missing sides are 7 cm and 3 cm.

2. 20 cm

3. 27 cm

4. 22 cm

5. 21 cm²

Find the area of a rectangle by multiplying the length and width together: 7 x 3 = 21 cm²

6. 24 cm²

The area of a triangle is $\frac{1}{2}$ x base x height. $\frac{1}{2}$ x 4 x 12 = 2 x 12 = 24 cm²

7. 125 cm

A regular pentagon has 5 equal sides so all 5 sides are 25 cm long. 25 + 25 + 25 + 25 + 25 (or 5 x 25) = 125 cm

8. 5 m

The area of the carpet = length x width. 75 = 15 x width, so width = 75 ÷ 15 = 5 m

9. 70 m

The playground is a regular octagon so all eight sides are the same length. The perimeter (560 m) divided by the number of sides (8) gives the length of each side: 560 ÷ 8 = 70 m

10. 16

From the left hand vertical side lengths you know the total height of the pen is 2 m + 4 m = 6 m. So the missing height on the right hand side of the pen must be 6 m – 4 m = 2 m. From the horizontal length at the top you know the total length of the pen is 10 m. So the missing length on the top left hand side is 10 m – 4 m – 4 m = 2 m.

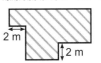

The sides of the pen are 10 m, 4 m, 4 m, 2 m, 4 m, 4 m, 2 m and 2 m. Add them to give a total of 32 m. Each panel is 2 m long so the number of panels needed is 32 ÷ 2 = 16 panels.

11. 3 cm

A kite has two pairs of equal sides, so all the sides at the top of the pattern are 2 cm.
The total length of all these sides is 6 × 2 = 12 cm.
The remaining sides together add up to
30 – 12 = 18 cm.
All the remaining 6 sides are the same length, so each side is 18 ÷ 6 = 3 cm

12. 36 cm²

Divide the shape into two sections as shown in the diagram.

rectangle   triangle

The area of the rectangle is 9 × 3 = 27 cm²
The height of the triangle is 15 – 9 = 6 cm The area of the triangle is ½ × 3 × 6 = 9 cm² So the total area of the shape is 27 + 9 = 36 cm²

13. 540 cm

The outer edge of the patio consists of 18 of the 30 cm sides.
So the perimeter is 18 × 30 = 540 cm

14. 22 cm

A rectangle with an area of 24 cm² must have sides of 2 cm and 12 cm, 3 cm and 8 cm, 4 cm and 6 cm or 1 cm and 24 cm. As the difference in the length of the sides is given as 5 cm then the rectangle must have sides of 3 cm and 8 cm. So its perimeter must be 3 + 3 + 8 + 8 (or (3 + 8) × 2) = 22 cm

15. 270 cm²

The three cardboard panels that make the tunnel each have the same dimensions and therefore the same area.
Area of each panel = 15 × 6 = 90 cm²
Total area = 3 × 90 = 270 cm²

16. 57 m²

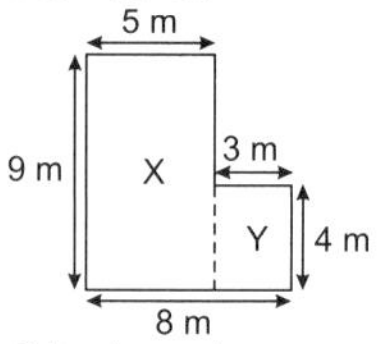

Split the garden into two rectangles — e.g. X and Y. X has sides 9 m and 5 m long so the area is 9 × 5 = 45 m².
Y has sides 3 m (8 – 5) and 4 m long so the area is 3 × 4 = 12 m².
The total area of the garden is 45 + 12 = 57 m²

17. 16 m²

You need to find the area of the triangle, which is ½ × base × height.
½ × 8 × 4 = 4 × 4 = 16 m²

18. 700 m²

The total area of the supermarket and the car park is 40 × 25 = 1000 m². The area of the supermarket is 20 × 15 = 300 m². Subtract the area of the supermarket from the total area to find the area of the car park: 1000 – 300 = 700 m²

19. 130 cm

The hole is made up of twenty two 5 cm edges and two 10 cm edges. The perimeter is:
(22 × 5) + (2 × 10) = 110 + 20 = 130 cm

20. 700 cm²

The area of each brick is 10 × 5 = 50 cm².
The hole fits 14 bricks, so the total area of the hole is 50 × 14 = 700 cm²

21. 3

The area of each wall is 4 × 2 = 8 m².
The total area of all 4 walls is 4 × 8 = 32 m².
Two tins of paint will be enough for 24 m² of wall (2 × 12 = 24) and three tins will be enough for 36 m² of wall (3 × 12 = 36).
So Martha needs to buy 3 tins of paint to have enough.

Page 34

1. H

H has one vertical and one horizontal line of symmetry.

2. W

W only has a vertical line of symmetry.

3. D

D only has a horizontal line of symmetry.

4. 3

R, F and N have no lines of symmetry.

5. D

Shape D has a horizontal mirror line.

6. B

B has rotational symmetry. It fits onto itself when you rotate it 180°.

7. D

The reflected shape has six sides (see diagram below). This means that it is a hexagon.

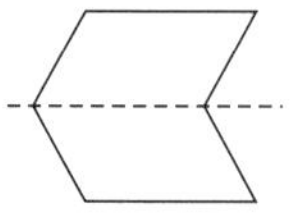

8. B

Pattern B is the only pattern that has a diagonal mirror line.

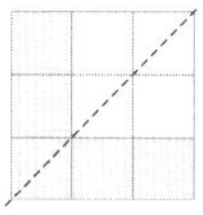

9. D

Pattern D has no lines of reflection but it fits onto itself when you rotate it through 180° (so it has rotational symmetry of order two).

10. E

Two more squares were shaded on the pattern as shown in the diagram below:

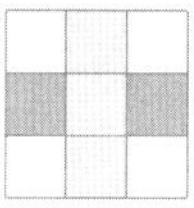

Its order of rotational symmetry has increased from 2 to 4.

Pages 35-36

1. 5

Shape A is a pentagonal prism. It has 5 rectangular faces.

2. E

A cube has six identical square faces.

3. D

A triangular prism has 2 triangular faces at each end and 3 rectangular faces in the middle. It also has 9 edges.

4. C

A cone has two faces but only one curved edge between the flat face and the curved face.

5. B

A square-based pyramid has five faces (1 square base + 4 triangular faces), 8 edges and 5 vertices (the vertices of the square plus the vertex at the tip of the pyramid).

6. 14 cm³

There are 14 cubes and the volume of each cube is 1 cm³. So the volume = 14 × 1 cm³ = 14 cm³

7. 84

7 cubes fit along the length of the box, 3 cubes fit across the width and 4 cubes can stack up the height of the box. 7 × 3 × 4 = 84 cubes

8. A

Net A is the only net that will fold up to make a cube.

9. B

A cuboid has more than 2 quadrilateral faces and it is also a prism. So it should go in the overlap of these two circles. It has no curved edges so it cannot go in the third circle.

10. D

The net folds up to make a square-based pyramid. Points Z and D will join together at the top of the pyramid.

11. D

Start by ruling out the nets where the same letters appear next to each other. So B and C can't be right. Then think about each of the other nets when they are folded. When nets A and E are folded, the two letter A's and the two letter B's will be next to each other.
When net D is folded, each pair of letters will be on opposite sides to each other.

12. B

The edges of each cube are 4 cm long.
The box is long enough to fit 40 ÷ 4 = 10 cubes.
The width of the box means you could fit 24 ÷ 4 = 6 rows in it.
So one layer of cubes = 6 × 10 = 60 cubes.
The box is high enough to fit 12 ÷ 4 = 3 layers of cubes in it.
So the total number of cubes = 3 × 60 = 180

13. B

There is no net for the cone. This diagram shows what the net of a cone might look like:

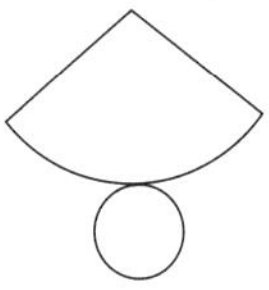

14. 8 cm

Volume = length × width × height
800 = 20 × width × 5
So 800 = 100 × width
So width = 800 ÷ 100 = 8 cm

15. 44 m³

Volume = length × width × height so the volume of the larger cuboid is 4 × 3 × 3 = 36 m³.
The volume of the small cube is 2 × 2 × 2 = 8 m³.
The total volume is 36 + 8 = 44 m³

Pages 37-38

For questions 1-5, you need to imagine the shape being flipped or rotated to find the option that matches the transformed shape.

1. C
2. A
3. D
4. B
5. E

6. 2 cm

7 sides of each of the outer 4 octagons make up the perimeter of the shape, plus 4 sides of the central octagon. So the total number of octagon sides that make up the shape
= (7 × 4) + 4 = 28 + 4 = 32.
The total perimeter of the shape = 64 cm.
So the length of each octagon side
= 64 ÷ 32 = 2 cm.

7. 18

The diagram below shows the painted faces on the stairs:

11 painted faces are visible.

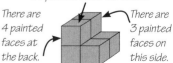

There are 4 painted faces at the back.   There are 3 painted faces on this side.

11 + 4 + 3 = 18 painted faces.

8. 11

You know the width of the model is 1 cm.
This is the same as the width of the bricks so all you need to worry about is how many bricks you would need to fit the length and the height. The diagram below shows how the model would be made:

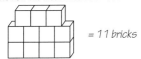

= 11 bricks

9. C

Imagine the shape being flipped from one side to the other of a vertical mirror line.

10. 6

6 tiles are needed:

11. 4.5 cm

Cynthia made the shape like this:

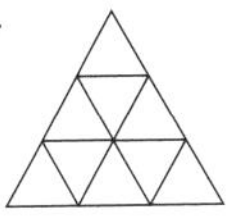

Each side of a tile is 1.5 cm, so the length of side x = 3 × 1.5 = 4.5 cm.

12. A

Focus on a particular part of the pattern and imagine where it will be when it's been rotated. For example,

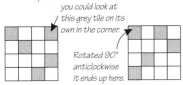

you could look at this grey tile on its own in the corner.

Rotated 90° anticlockwise it ends up here.

Do this with two or three parts of the pattern to check the option you've chosen is right.

13. E

When shape Z is rotated through 90° clockwise you get shape E.

14. D

A plan view is what the shape looks like from directly above.

15. E

You would be able to see two bobbles on the robot's head on the side elevation of robot E.

Page 39

To find the coordinates for questions 1-5, move along the x-axis to find the horizontal position of the point. Then move up the y-axis to find the vertical position.

1. (9, 7)
2. (5, 11)
3. (4, 4)
4. (8, 2)
5. (2, 9)

6. (4, 9)

When you move 4 squares west from point A you get to the point (4, 2). When you move 7 squares north from (4, 2) you reach the point (4, 9).

7. A

To be parallel with JK, the line must follow the dotted shown. Plot the coordinates you're given until you find the pair that sit on this line. The only option given that's on this line is point (-7, 0).

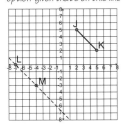

8. C

Only points with x and y-coordinates greater than 2 but less than 7 will lie within the square. (8, 4) has an x-coordinate greater than 7 so is outside of the square.

9. (6, 15)

W is vertically below point (6, 19) (top of the pentagon). So its x-coordinate is also 6.
W is also in a horizontal line with points (3, 15) and (9, 15), so its y-coordinate is 15.

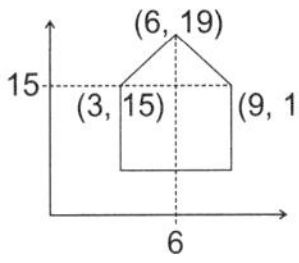

Page 40

1. (8, 6)

The rotated triangle is shown in the diagram. The coordinates of point B are now at (8, 6).

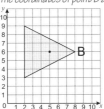

2. B

The diagram shows the reflected shape. The coordinates of the reflected point G are (-5, 4).

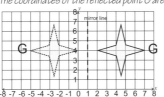

3. (12, 8)

The point at (1, 8) has moved to (4, 10). The x-coordinate has increased by 3 and the y-coordinate has increased by 2 (so the shape has moved 3 squares right and 2 squares up). Point C was previously at (9, 6) so its new x-coordinate is 9 + 3 = 12, and its new y-coordinate is 6 + 2 = 8.

4. (5, 1)

You know the shape is a square so the length of all the sides must be the same. The top line has coordinates (-2, 6) and (1, 6) so its length is 3. Before the translation point W will have the same x-coordinate as the point above it (1) but the y-coordinate will decrease by 3, so its coordinates must be (1, 3).
After the translation the x-coordinate of point X has increased by 4 and the y-coordinate has decreased by 2. So after the translation the x-coordinate of the image of point W will be 1 + 4 = 5 and the y-coordinate will be 3 – 2 = 1.

5. (2, 3)

The diagram shows the shape rotated 180° clockwise about point A. The coordinates of the image of point X are (2, 3).

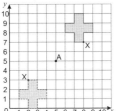

6. (2, 9)

The diagram shows the new shape reflected in the mirror line. The the image of point X is at (2, 9).

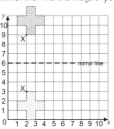

Section Six
— Units and Measurements

Pages 41-42

For questions 1-4, pick the unit that best matches each object.

1. B

A rabbit is usually no taller than 30 cm, so you'd measure it in centimetres.

2. A

It's a long way between London and Liverpool, so you'd measure the distance in kilometres.

3. C

Buildings are taller than the average person, so you'd measure their height in metres.

4. D

The thickness of a coin is very small, so you'd measure it in millimetres.

5. 1560 g

1 kilogram = 1000 grams
1.56 × 1000 = 1560 grams

6. 2500 ml

1 litre = 1000 millilitres
2.5 × 1000 = 2500 millilitres

7. 1.28 m

1 metre = 100 centimetres
128 ÷ 100 = 1.28 metres

8. 15 300 m

1 kilometre = 1000 metres
15.3 × 1000 = 15 300 metres

9. 4.5 kg

1 kilogram = 1000 grams
4500 ÷ 1000 = 4.5 kilograms

10. C

2.54 kg, 5400 g, 5.4 kg and 54 kg are far too heavy for a pencil. The most likely answer is 5.4 g.

11. 500 g

Mass of one bag = 16 kg ÷ 32 = 0.5 kg.
You need to give your answer in grams.
1 kg = 1000 g, so 0.5 × 1000 = 500 g

12. D

An egg cup, a teacup and a teaspoon are all very small and wouldn't hold 1 litre of water. A dustbin is very large and would hold much more than 1 litre of water. The most likely answer is a small saucepan.

13. 175 g

The scale increases by 25 g at every notch. The needle on the scale is pointing one notch before 200 g, so 200 g – 25 g = 175 g

14. 350 g

Both parcels weigh 175 grams. Together they will weigh 175 × 2 = 350 grams.

15. 11

This can be calculated using trial and error. It's easy to see that 10 parcels would weigh 1750 g, or 1.75 kg. 11 parcels would weigh 1750 g + 175 g = 1925 g or 1.925 kg.
12 parcels would weigh 2.1 kg. So the largest number of parcels you can send in one sack is 11.

16. 26.4 m

Convert all lengths to metres. 1 metre = 100 cm, so 650 cm is 650 ÷ 100 = 6.5 m. Add all the lengths together: 6.5 + 7.6 + 12.3 = 26.4 m

17. E

1 litre = 1000 ml, so 1.5 litres is 1500 ml. 400 ml is about a quarter of 1500 ml, so the correct bottle will be about three quarters full.

18. £25.50

The total distance Roberto travelled is 24 + 15 + 12 = 51 km. In the taxi it costs 25p to travel 500 m, so to travel 1 km would be 2 × 25p = 50p. The total cost would be 51 × 50p = 2550p = £25.50

19. 200 ml

12 × 150 ml = 1800 ml 2 litres = 1000 ml × 2 = 2000 ml So 2000 ml − 1800 ml = 200 ml

20. D

There are 4 kg of meatballs, so twice as much pasta would be 4 × 2 = 8 kg. Altogether there is 4 + 8 = 12 kg of meatballs and pasta. Each serving is 250 g, so 4 servings would be 4 × 250 g = 1000 g = 1 kg. So there are 12 × 4 = 48 servings in 12 kg.

21. 15 litres

270 ÷ 9 = 30, so Mrs Conway's car needs 30 lots of ½ a litre of petrol. 30 lots of ½ a litre is 30 × ½ = 15 litres

22. 13.5 m

10 mm = 1 cm, so a 15 mm sticker is 15 ÷ 10 = 1.5 cm long. Caroline used 250 3 cm stickers, and 400 1.5 cm stickers. Total length = (250 × 3) + (400 × 1.5) = 750 + 600 = 1350 cm 1 m = 100 cm, so 1350 ÷ 100 = 13.5 m

23. 4.2 m

1 cm = 0.01 m. Therefore 80 cm = 0.8 m. The shape around the box is a rectangle. The perimeter of a rectangle is the sum of all four sides. The perimeter is 0.8 + 0.8 + 1.3 + 1.3 = 4.2 m

24. 140

Each sticker is 3 cm in length. Convert the perimeter of the box into cm by multiplying by 100. 4.2 × 100 = 420 cm. The number of stickers required is 420 ÷ 3 = 140.

25. 2.1 m

Each small sticker is 15 mm. This can be converted into cm by dividing by 10. 15 ÷ 10 = 1.5 cm. The length of stickers around the box is 1.5 × 140 = 210 cm. This can be converted into m by dividing by 100. The perimeter is 210 ÷ 100 = 2.1 m.

Pages 43-44

1. 3:45 or 15:45

The hour hand is pointing between 3 and 4, so the hour is 3. The minute hand is pointing at 9, which is 45 minutes past the hour. So the time is 3:45.

2. E

If the number of hours on a 24-hour clock is between 13 and 23, you can work out the time in the 12-hour clock by subtracting 12 from the number of hours. 19 − 12 = 7, so the time on clock A is 7:20 pm. On clock E the hour hand is pointing between 7 and 8, so the hour is 7. The minute hand is pointing at 4, which is 20 minutes past the hour.

3. D

Twenty to seven in the evening is 6:40 pm. The 12-hour clocks do not show this time because none of them have their hour hand between 6 and 7. On a 24-hour clock, 6 o'clock will be shown by 6 + 12 = 18. One digital clock shows 18:40, which is the same as 6:40 pm.

4. 18:45

Clock A is 35 minutes further ahead than it should be, so you need to subtract 35 minutes from the time shown. Do this in two parts, first subtract 20 minutes from 19:20 to get to 19:00. Then subtract 15 minutes from 19:00 to get to 18:45.

5. B

There are 60 minutes in an hour, so 90 minutes is 1 hour and 30 minutes. Add 1 hour to ten past 8 and you get ten past 9, add 30 mins to that and you get 9:40. The clock showing 9:40 is B. The hour hand is pointing between 9 and 10, so the hour is 9. The minute hand is pointing to 8, which is 40 minutes past the hour.

6. 25 minutes

The number 35 bus leaves the Bus Station at 10:15 and arrives at Bank Street at 10:40. There are 25 minutes from 10:15 to 10:40.

7. 35 minutes

The number 42 bus leaves the bus station at 11:25 and arrives at Bigsby Road at 12:00. Add 5 minutes to get from 11:25 to 11:30 and add 30 minutes to get from 11:30 to 12:00. 5 + 30 = 35 minutes

8. 27 minutes

The number 35 bus leaves Bank Street at 10:40 and arrives at Clayton Close at 11:07. Add 20 minutes to get from 10:40 to 11:00 and add 7 minutes to get from 11:00 to 11:07. 20 + 7 = 27 minutes

9. 7 minutes

The number 35 bus leaves the Bus Station at 10:15 and arrives at the Hospital at 11:20. So add 1 hour to 10:15 to get to 11:15 and add 5 minutes to get from 11:15 to 11:20. 1 hour = 60 minutes, 60 + 5 = 65 minutes in total. The 42 bus leaves the Bus Station at 11:25 and arrives at the hospital at 12:37. So add 1 hour to 11:25 to get to 12:25 and add 12 minutes to get from 12:25 to 12:37. 1 hour = 60 minutes, 60 + 12 = 72 minutes in total. So the difference between the times the buses take is 72 − 65 = 7 minutes.

10. D

The closest months to August are October and July. 28th July is less than a month from 15th August, but 4th October is more than a month away. So the answer is 28th July.

11. D

Count on 12 days from 27th September. There are 30 days in September, so 3 of the days will be in September. 12 − 3 = 9, so that leaves 9 days in October. Mary's birthday will be 9th October.

12. 10:13

Kat allowed 12 minutes for the walk and 5 minutes to find her seat. 12 + 5 = 17 minutes, so she must have left 17 minutes before 10:30. 10:30 − 17 minutes = 10:13

13. 11 minutes

Jo left 16 minutes after Kat. If Kat left at 10:13 then Jo must have left at 10:13 + 16 minutes = 10:29 It took her 9 + 3 = 12 minutes to get to the theatre and find her seat, meaning she was in her seat at 10:29 + 12 minutes = 10:41 The play started at 10:30, making Jo 41 − 30 = 11 minutes late.

14. A

There are 60 seconds in a minute, so 3 × 60 = 180 seconds. Work out ¾ of a minute: 60 ÷ 4 = 15, 15 × 3 = 45 seconds. So 3¾ minutes = 180 + 45 = 225 seconds

15. E

25 minutes to midnight is 11:35 pm using the 12-hour clock. To find a time after 1 pm on a 24-hour clock you need to add 12 to the hours. So 11 pm would be 11 + 12 = 23 11:35 pm is 23:35.

16. 6 hours and 30 minutes

Mr Smith started at quarter to ten in the morning, which is 9:45 am. Add on 15 minutes to get to 10 am. Add on 7 hours to get to 5 pm. Then add on 15 minutes to get to 5:15 pm. 15 minutes + 7 hours + 15 minutes = 7 hours and 30 minutes. He took 1 hour off for lunch. 7 hours and 30 minutes − 1 hour = 6 hours and 30 minutes

17. 45 minutes

3 people took swimming lessons, so you need to divide 2 hours and 15 minutes by 3. Two hours is 2 × 60 = 120 minutes 120 + 15 = 135 minutes 135 ÷ 3 = 45 minutes

18. Friday

You know that 18th May is a Tuesday, so every 7th day after 18th May will also be a Tuesday. Add 7 days on at a time to 18th May. Remember, there are 31 days in May. 18th May + 7 days = 25th May 25th May + 7 days = 1st June 1st June + 7 days = 8th June 8th June + 7 days = 15th June 15th June is a Tuesday, now add on three days to Tuesday to find what day of the week 18th June is. 1st day = Wednesday, 2nd day = Thursday and 3rd day = Friday.

19. 4 hours 10 minutes

In one week she spends: 25 × 5 = 125 minutes doing her homework. In two weeks she spends: 2 × 125 = 250 minutes. 1 hour = 60 minutes, so 4 hours would be 4 × 60 minutes = 240 minutes. So she would spend 4 hours and 10 minutes doing her homework.

20. D

Javier took 2 hours and 20 minutes, so you need to find the pair of times which has this difference. The answer is 11:35 and 13:55. Add two hours to 11:35 to get to 13:35 and add 20 minutes to get from 13:35 to 13:55.

21. 11:10 and 13:00

Molly visited the zoo on a Thursday in February, so the zoo was open between 10:30 and 15:30. Molly arrived 40 minutes after it opened. Add 30 minutes to get from 10:30 am to 11:00, then add 10 minutes to get from 11:00 to 11:10. She left 2½ hours before it closed. Subtract 30 minutes from 15:30 to get to 15:00 and subtract 2 hours from 15:00 to get to 13:00. So Molly was at the zoo between 11:10 and 13:00.

22. 11:02

Spelling usually finishes at 10:50. 12 minutes later than this is 10:50 + 12 minutes = 11:00 + 2 minutes = 11:02

23. 95 minutes

Jessica's literacy lesson starts at 11:10, so subtract 35 minutes from 11:10. Subtract 30 minutes to get to 10:40 and then subtract 5 minutes to get to 10:35. Lunch starts at 12:15 and Jessica returns to school 5 minutes before the start of lunch, so she returns at 12:10. Work out the time difference between 10:35 and 12:10. 10:35 to 11:00 is 25 minutes. 11:00 to 12:00 is 1 hour = 60 minutes. 12:00 to 12:10 is 10 minutes. 25 + 60 + 10 = 95 minutes

24. 16:05

From question 23, Jessica was away from school for 95 minutes. Her music lesson is 95 – 10 = 85 minutes. This is equal to 1 hour and 25 minutes. Add this time on in parts:
1 hour on from 14:40 is 15:40,
20 minutes on from 15:40 is 16:00 and
5 minutes on from 16:00 is 16:05.

Section Seven
— Mixed Problems

Pages 45-46

1. 50%

The black and silver segments make up half of the pie chart (135° + 45° = 180°). That means that 50% of the people drove black or silver cars.

2. 1/3

The total angle of the segments for blue and red cars is 90° + 30° = 120°. This as a fraction of the entire chart is $\frac{120}{360}$ which can be simplified to $\frac{1}{3}$.

3. 8

To find how long it will take to eat 40% of the bag you need to work out what $\frac{1}{20}$ is as a percentage. Convert $\frac{1}{20}$ into an equivalent fraction with a denominator of 100. Multiply the numerator and the denominator by 5 to get $\frac{5}{100}$. That means that $\frac{1}{20}$ is the same as 5%. It takes Greg 1 day to eat 5% of the bag, so it takes him 40 ÷ 5 = 8 days to eat 40% of the bag.

4. Blueberry

The modal value is the value which is the most common. The pictogram shows more people chose Blueberry pie than any other pie, so it is the modal flavour of pie.

5. 25p

Convert £4.50 into pence by multiplying it by 100, 4.5 × 100 = 450p. 9 days worth of seeds cost 450p, so 1 day's worth of seeds costs 450 ÷ 9 = 50p. 2 cups of seeds are used each day, so the cost of 1 cup is 50p ÷ 2 = 25p.

6. £198

150 cm = 1.5 m.
The area of the hallway is 6 × 1.5 = 9 m²
The cost of the carpet is £22 × 9 = £198

7. 2000 litres

From 8:20 am to 9 am is 40 minutes.
From 9 am to 10 am is 60 minutes.
40 + 60 = 100 minutes. 20 litres goes into the pool every minute, so 100 × 20 = 2000 litres

8. £400

The area of the yard is 5 × 8 = 40 m²
Mr Taylor wants to turf half of it which is 40 ÷ 2 = 20 m². 4 m² of turf costs £80. He will need 20 ÷ 4 = 5 rolls of turf to cover half of his yard. 5 rolls of turf will cost 5 × £80 = £400

9. B

Angles on a straight line add up to 180°. So x = 180° – 75° – 60° = 45° 45° × 4 = 180°, so x is $\frac{1}{4}$ of 180°.

10. £100

If the mean of Mrs Farooq's gas bills is £80, then the total is 4 × £80 = £320. Reading off the chart, July's bill = £40, October's = £60 and January's = £120. £40 + £60 + £120 = £220, so the bill in April is £320 – £220 = £100

11. £80

The range is the difference between the largest and smallest values. The smallest value is for July (£40). The largest value is for January (£120). The difference is £120 – £40 = £80

12. 310 kg

If the mean weight of the crop from the 5 trees is 320 kg, then the total weight would be 5 × 320 kg = 1600 kg The total crop from four trees is 370 + 280 + 330 + 310 = 1290 kg. The crop from the 5th tree will be 1600 – 1290 = 310 kg

13. C

Volume = length × width × height So the volume of the container is 25 × 10 × 10 = 2500 cm³. The container is filled with 1000 cm³ of water, so the fraction of the container filled with water is $\frac{1000}{2500} = \frac{10}{25}$.
To find this as a percentage you need to turn it into an equivalent fraction with 100 as the denominator. Multiply the numerator and the denominator by 4 to get $\frac{40}{100}$ = 40%

14. B

If you read off the bar chart the number of German books is 8. There are 18 + 8 + 14 = 40 books in total, so the probability of picking up a German book is $\frac{8}{40}$. This can be simplified to $\frac{1}{5}$ if you divide the numerator and the denominator by 8.

15. 10

Find how much washing liquid is needed per bucket. 1 litre = 1000 ml, so 500 ml is 0.5 litres. In 6 litres there are 12 lots of 0.5 litres (12 × 0.5 = 6). So the total amount of washing liquid in 1 bucket = 12 × 5 ml = 60 ml. The bottle contains 600 ml of washing liquid, so 600 ml ÷ 60 ml = 10 buckets.

16. B

The pattern uses 2 hexagons and 4 squares (which have been cut into 8 triangles). The area of 1 hexagon is H, so the area of 2 hexagons is 2H. The area of 1 square is S, so the area of 4 squares = 4S. Altogether the area of Hannah's pattern is 2H + 4S.

17. A

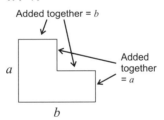

The two unknown sides opposite to the labelled side a add together to make a. The two unknown sides opposite to the labelled side b add together to make b. So the perimeter is 2a + 2b.

18. B

Find which rule will give the first number in the sequence. For the first number n = 1, only 2 rules will give 5 as an answer. If n = 1, 7n – 2 = 7 – 2 = 5, and n + 4 = 1 + 4 = 5. Try these rules for n = 2: 7n – 2 = 14 – 2 = 12, and n + 4 = 2 + 4 = 6. Only 7n – 2 gives the right number for both terms.

19. 25

If the sequence value is 173, it can be written that 173 = 7n – 2. Adding 2 to each side gives 175 = 7n and so n = 175 ÷ 7 = 25

20. £66.50

Gerald is paid £3.50 for every half hour, so he is paid £3.50 × 2 = £7.00 for every hour. Next work out how many hours he was at work for. From 6:20 am to 4:20 pm is 10 hours. From 4:20 pm to 4:50 pm is 30 minutes, or half an hour. So he was at work for a total of 10 and a half hours. He took 1 hour unpaid for his lunch so he got paid for 9 and a half hours work. He was paid 9 × £7.00 = £63.00 for the nine hours, and £3.50 for the half hour. So he earned £63.00 + £3.50 = £66.50 in total.

21. 360 ml

From 4 pm on Monday to 4 pm on Tuesday is 24 hours. From 4 pm on Tuesday to 4 pm on Wednesday is 24 hours, but subtract 2 hours to get back to 2 pm. So that's 24 – 2 = 22 hours. 24 + 22 = 46 hours. 46 ÷ 2 = 23 doses, but this doesn't include her first dose, so the total number of doses = 23 + 1 = 24 doses. 1 dose = 15 ml, so 24 × 15 = 360 ml

Assessment Test 1

Section A
Pages 47-50

1. 25.5 cm

There are 10 spaces between 24 cm and 26 cm. So each space is worth 2 ÷ 10 = 0.2 cm. The arrow is pointing halfway between 25.4 and 25.6. Half of the gap between 25.4 and 25.6 is 0.2 ÷ 2 = 0.1 cm, so the number the arrow is pointing to is 25.4 + 0.1 = 25.5 cm

2. C

Angle y is bigger than a right angle (90°), so it can't be 60° (B) or 90° (D). It is smaller than a straight line (180°), so it can't be 180° (A). 175° (E) is almost a straight line and angle y is smaller than a straight line by more than 5°. So that leaves C as the only possible answer.

3. A

You need to use BODMAS to work out the initial answer and each option.
6 × 2 + 12 = 12 + 12 = 24
A: 8 × 3 = 24, 48 – 24 = 24 — so A is the answer.
B: 11 × 2 = 22, 3 + 22 = 25
C: 3 × 7 = 21
D: 24 ÷ 2 = 12, 12 – 1 = 11
E: 4 × 4 = 16, 2 + 16 = 18

4. £7.08

£5 + £2 = £7
5p + 2p + 1p = 8p
£7 + 8p = £7.08

5. D

Scalene triangles have three different sides and three different angles. Rhombuses, kites, regular pentagons and isosceles triangles have at least two equal sides and at least two equal angles.

6. £8.91

Round each 99p up to £1 by adding 1p, then multiply by 9: £1 × 9 = £9. You added 9 × 1p to the total cost, so subtract the extra 9p: £9 – 9p = £8.91

7. B

In 45.952, 9 is in the tenths column. Look at the number in the next column to the right (the hundredths). It is 5, so round the 9 tenths up to 10 tenths. 10 tenths is one unit, so the rounded number is 46.0

8. 16:50

When using the 24 hour clock, the hours in the afternoon, i.e: after 12 noon, increase from 13 to 23. Ten to five in the afternoon is equivalent to fifty minutes past four. Four o'clock is 4 hours after 12 noon so is 4 + 12 = 16:00. To make this fifty minutes past four, 16:00 + 0:50 = 16:50

9. A

The cake is cut into 20 slices and 16 are given away. This leaves 20 – 16 = 4 slices. As a fraction of the overall cake, this is $\frac{4}{20}$. The highest common factor of both the numerator and the denominator is 4: 4 ÷ 4 = 1, 20 ÷ 4 = 5. The amount of cake left over is $\frac{1}{5}$.

10. 1900

The tens column is the second column from the right. This is 9, which rounds up to 10. This increases the value of the hundreds column by one making the answer 1900.

11. B

The customer is charged £50 for the job, plus the number of hours (h) multiplied by £25.
So the cost = 50 + 25 × h, or 50 + 25h.

12. 5

Work through your 5 times table until you come to first number greater than 24.
5 × 5 = 25, so 5 tents would be enough.

13. 1404

There are 3 lots of 2808 (multiplication is repeated addition), which is equal to 6 lots of something.
6 is double 3, so halve 2808 to find the missing number: Half of 2808 is 1404.
So 2808 + 2808 + 2808 = 1404 × 6

14. C

On the graph, you can see that the February sales are lowest. The only game for which this is true is Croc Chase.

15. 9

The whole circle represents 36 children. The yellow area of the pie chart is 90° or a quarter of the circle. ¼ of 36 is 36 ÷ 4 = 9.
9 children wore yellow hats.

16. £1.07

One way of doing £10 – £8.93 is to count up from 8.93 to 10 on a quick sketch of a number line:

0.07 + 1 = £1.07

17. 61

You can't calculate the blue team total straight away. One method is to calculate the number of points won by the Year 5 blue team first (90 – 27 – 32 = 31). Then use this to find the blue team total (31 + 30 = 61).

Team	Year 5	Year 6	Total
Red	27	50	77
Yellow	32	25	57
Blue	**31**	30	**61**
Total	90	105	

Alternatively, find the grand total by adding the numbers on the bottom row (90 + 105 = 195). Then use this to find the blue team total: (195 – 77 – 57 = 61).

18. 6p

10% of 40p is 40 ÷ 10 = 4p. So the cost of each packet is 40 – 4 = 36p.
There are 6 bears in each packet, so the cost of each bear is 36 ÷ 6 = 6p.

19. D

The spinner can be split into 10 equal sections. 6 out of the 10 sections are spotty, so the probability of the spinner landing on a spotty section is ⁶/₁₀ or ³/₅.
This means that more than half of the segments are spotty, so there is more chance of the spinner landing on a spotty section than any other section.

20. D

The right angled triangle has 1 right angle, the square has 4 right angles. None of the other shapes have any.

21. D

Prime numbers are only divisible by themselves and 1.
47 = 1 × 47
55 = 1 × 55 and 5 × 11
42 = 1 × 42, 2 × 21, 3 × 14 and 6 × 7
41 = 1 × 41
58 = 1 × 58 and 2 × 29
63 = 1 × 63, 3 × 21 and 7 × 9
62 = 1 × 62 and 2 × 31
73 = 1 × 73

22. D

Look at the top right corner of the rectangle, and follow the instructions to see where it moves to.

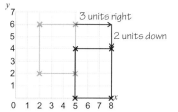

The top right corner would now be at point (8, 4). This coordinate is only in option D, so that's the answer.

23. 6

Write the sizes out in order: 5, 5, 6, 6, 6, 7, 7
The median is the middle value. There are 7 numbers, so the median is the 4ᵗʰ number in the list, 6.

24. 28 cm

The length of each side of the hexagons is 2 cm. The outer edge of the shape is made up of 14 of these sides. So the total length = 2 × 14 = 28 cm

25. 36.6 g

¼ tin has 12.2 g of carbohydrate.
³/₄ is 3 times as much as ¼,
so 12.2 g × 3 = 36.6 g of carbohydrate.

26. 10:05

The first train after 9 am from Chapel Street is at 9:15. Reading down the same column of the table, it arrives in Lanston at 10:05.

27. C

A, B, D and E can be split into two of the trapezium-shaped tiles shown. C can't — the tiles overlap.

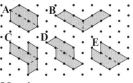

28. A

The only days on which there is a meat pie and a non-apple dessert are Monday and Friday.
This is two days out of five, so the probability is ²/₅.

29. –8 °C

The temperature drops from 1 °C to –2 °C, which is a drop of 3 °C, from Tuesday to Wednesday.
Twice this is 3 °C × 2 = 6 °C.
6 °C lower than –2 °C is –8 °C.

30. D

Imagine folding the net up to make a cuboid.
Corner D will touch X.

Section B
Pages 50-52

1. 0.9 kg

First calculate the mass of the 7 peaches:
7 × 200 g = 1400 g. 1 kg = 1000 g, so 1400 g = 1.4 kg
The mass of the basket: 2.3 – 1.4 = 0.9 kg

2. 2.15 kg

In question 1, the basket was found to weigh 0.9 kg. 3 peaches are exchanged for apples.
The basket will still contain 7 – 3 = 4 peaches.
Each peach weighs 200 g. The weight of peaches in the basket is 200 × 4 = 800g. This is equal to 800 ÷ 1000 = 0.8 kg.
One apple weighs ³/₄ of the weight of one peach. (200 ÷ 4) × 3 = 150 g. The weight of 3 apples is 150 × 3 = 450 g. This is equal to 0.45 kg.
The weight of the basket and its contents is 0.9 + 0.8 + 0.45 = 2.15 kg

3. 0.45 m

The range is the difference between the highest and lowest values. The furthest Andy jumped was 5.25 m. His shortest jump was 4.80 m.
The range is 5.25 – 4.80 = 0.45 m

4. 4.75 m

The mode is the most frequently occurring value. Roger jumped 4.75 m twice.

5. 5.00 m

The mean is found by adding all the values and dividing the sum by the number of pieces of data.
5.25 + 5.00 + 4.90 + 4.95 + 4.80 + 5.10 = 30.00
So the mean is 30.00 ÷ 6 = 5.00 m.

6. 4.90 m

The median is found by arranging the data in numerical order and selecting the middle number.
In order, Roger's jumps are:
4.70 , 4.75 , 4.75 , 5.05 , 5.10 , 5.30 .
The middle two values are 4.75 and 5.05.
So the median is the midpoint of these two values.
4.75 + 5.05 = 9.80, 9.80 ÷ 2 = 4.90 m.

7. 32

To find the answer you need to work backwards from 131. You're told that a number was divided by 2 to make 131 — so the number was 131 × 2 = 262. You're told that 6 was added to a number to make 262, so subtract 6 from 262, 262 – 6 = 256. You're told that a number was multiplied by 8 to make 256, so divide 256 by 8.
256 ÷ 8 = 32

8. 50 minutes

Divide 1 litre by 20 ml to see how many minutes it will take.
1 litre = 1000 ml. So work out 1000 ÷ 20.
You can make this easier to work out by dividing both numbers by 10, so that's 100 ÷ 2 = 50 mins

9. 10%

The amount of discount received off the original price of £27.50 was £27.50 – £24.75 = £2.75.
2.75 = 27.50 ÷ 10, so the discount is ¹/₁₀ of the original price. This is the same as 10%.

10. 2:1

There are 8 circles and 4 squares.
This is a ratio of 8 : 4.
This can be simplified by dividing both sides by 4.

11. 1:1

There are 2 grey squares and 2 white squares.
This is a ratio of 2 : 2, or 1 : 1 in its simplest form.

12. C

There are 3 white circles and 12 shapes in total.
This gives a fraction of ³/₁₂.
This can be simplified by dividing the numerator and denominator by 3 to give ¼.

13. 500 g

The ingredients given make 12 cakes.
40 cakes = 3 lots of 12 cakes + 4 cakes.
4 cakes = ⅓ of 12 cakes. She will need to multiply the amount of butter given by 3⅓.
You can partition 3⅓ into 3 + ⅓.
⅓ × 150 g = 150 ÷ 3 = 50 g
150 g × 3 = 450 g
So the total amount of butter is 450 g + 50 g = 500 g

14. 70

We are told 240 g of flour makes 12 cupcakes.
Each cupcake requires 240g ÷ 12 = 20 g of flour. 1.4 kg is equivalent to 1.4 × 1000 = 1400 g of flour. The number of cupcakes that can be made with 1400 g of flour is 1400 ÷ 20 = 140 ÷ 2 = 70 cupcakes.

15. 26

Read the number of children who chose plum and the number who chose pear off the horizontal axis. The number who chose plum is halfway between 28 and 32 so 30 children chose plum. The number who chose pear = 4. Subtract to find how many more children chose plum than pear: 30 – 4 = 26.

16. A

4 children chose pear and 24 children chose apple, so 24 + 4 = 28 children chose either pear or apple. For a fruit to be half as popular, it would have to be chosen 28 ÷ 2 = 14 times. Orange was chosen 14 times. Peach was chosen 28 times. Plum was chosen 30 times. Banana was chosen 18 times. Therefore the answer is orange.

17. £17.40

Bella gets 6 boxes of 20 cards for 4 × £3.90. Partition £3.90 into £3 + 90p 4 × £3 = £12, 4 × 90p = £3.60 £12 + £3.60 = £15.60. She also gets a box of 12 envelopes for £1.80 Total cost = £15.60 + £1.80 = £17.40

18. (4, 2)

Here is the route she follows:

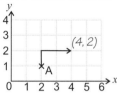

Don't forget — the x-axis coordinate always goes first when you're writing coordinates.

19. (1, 0)

Here is the route she follows from the point (4, 2):

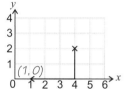

20. £15

If Amanda spent 60% of her pocket money, she must have 40% left. 40% = £6, so 10% would be £6 ÷ 4 = £1.50. So 100% would be 10 × £1.50 = £15

21. 11:05

If Kate travels at 60 km/h, she will cover 2 × 60 = 120 km in 2 hours. She then goes a further 15 km (135 – 120). 15 km is ¼ of 60 km, so she will travel 15 km in ¼ of an hour. She travels for 2¼ hours in total. If she starts at 8:50 am, 2 hours later will be 10:50 am and 15 minutes after this will be 11:05 am.

22. E

The mean of a set of four numbers is the total of the numbers divided by 4. So if the mean is 4, the total of the numbers is 4 × 4 = 16. The two sides you can see add up to 11 (3 + 8). So the two hidden sides must add up to 16 – 11 = 5. The only pair of numbers in the answer choices that add up to 5 is 1 and 4.

23. 8.1 litres

Convert 900 ml into litres by dividing by 1000. 900 ÷ 1000 = 0.9 litres Add up the three volumes:

$$\begin{array}{r} 4.4 \\ 0.9 \\ + 2.8 \\ \hline 8.1 \\ \scriptstyle 2 \end{array}$$

24. 85%

To convert from fractions into percent, multiply the numerator and denominator by the same number until the denominator equals 100. The numerator is now equal to the percentage. 100 ÷ 20 = 5. Therefore you need to multiply the numerator by 5 to get the percentage. 17 × 5 = 85%.

25. 67°

Put n = 46° into the formula. m = (180 – 46) ÷ 2 m = 134 ÷ 2 = 67°

26. 72 m²

To calculate the area of one triangle: (6 × 4) ÷ 2 = 12 m². The playground is made up of six triangles so the total area is 12 × 6 = 72 m²

27. 2

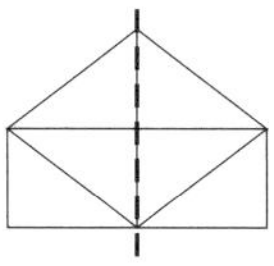

There is 1 line of symmetry shown above with the dashed line. The playground has rotational symmetry of order 1. So the answer is 1 + 1 = 2.

28. 19 m³

Volume = width × height × length The volumes of the cube and the cuboid can be calculated separately. Cuboid: 5.5 × 1 × 2 = 11 m³ Cube: 2 × 2 × 2 = 8 m³ The total volume is the sum of the volumes of the cube and cuboid. 11 + 8 = 19 m³

29. 375 g

First find out how many 2ps make up £1. £1 = 100p, so there are 100 ÷ 2 = 50 coins in each pile. Each pile should weigh 50 × 7.5 = 375 g.

30. 75 kg

From question 29 you know that £1 of 2p's weighs 375 g = 0.375 kg. Multiply this by 200 to get the weight of £200 of 2p's. 0.375 × 200 = 0.375 × 100 × 2 = 37.5 kg × 2 = 75 kg

Assessment Test 2

Section A
Pages 53-56

1. D

There are 8 segments and 3 are shaded. This is the fraction ³⁄₈.

2. 34 minutes

The range is the difference between the slowest time and the fastest time. The slowest time was 156 minutes and the fastest was 122 minutes. 156 – 122 = 34

3. B

You need to find the piece that is the right size and shape to fit in the gap. Shape B has been rotated by 180° but is the only shape that fits in the gap.

4. A

A small can of beans weighs around 250 g. All of the other weights are either too small or too large.

5. B

21² is 21 × 21. You can estimate the answer by rounding the numbers to the nearest 10 and working out 20 × 20. 20 × 20 = 400. The only realistic option is B: 441.

6. B

For B, the dial is split into 8 parts and 1 kg is at the 4th point, halfway round the scale. This means each point on the scale represents 1 kg ÷ 4 = 250 g. As the arrow is pointing at the 3rd point, it is pointing at 3 × 250 g = 750 g.

7. 9 m

To find the length of 20 scarves you need to multiply 45 cm by 20: 45 × 20 = 900 cm. There are 100 cm in 1 m, so 900 cm = 9 m

8. 145.75 cm

The difference between 145.6 and 145.9 is 145.9 – 145.6 = 0.3. 0.3 ÷ 2 = 0.15 so the halfway point between the two numbers will be 145.6 + 0.15 = 145.75

9. 6

Dogs have 2½ symbols and fish have 1 symbol so the difference between them is 1½ symbols. Each symbol in the pictogram is equal to 4 people. So half of a symbol is 4 ÷ 2 = 2 people. 1½ symbols is equal to 4 people + 2 people = 6 people

10. B

Elsa has 7 + 8 + 3 = 18 sweets to start with. She eats 2 chocolates so there are 16 sweets left (18 – 2 = 16). There are still 8 toffees left, so the probability of picking a toffee next is ⁸⁄₁₆. Divide the numerator and denominator by 8 to find ⁸⁄₁₆ = ½.

11. E

The y-axis is the vertical axis so the coordinates of the reflected point A are (2, 2) (see the diagram).

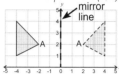

12. £45

If you add up the portions that Eloise, Lucinda and Jennifer get all together, 5 + 3 + 2 = 10. Calculate the amount in one share: £150 ÷ 10 = £15 Eloise, Lucinda and Jennifer share the money in a 5 : 3 : 2 ratio. Lucinda receives a share of 3, and therefore gets 15 × 3 = £45

13. E

The number 26 is an even number, but it isn't a multiple of 3 or a multiple of 7, so it can't be placed in the sorting table.

14. C

When you rotate the clear pentagon by 180° it looks like this:

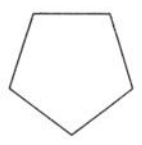

The only option where the clear pentagon looks like this is option C.

15. 72 minutes

Work out the length of time that the journey takes on each bus. On Bus A the journey takes 9:44 to 10:44 = 60 minutes plus 10:44 to 10:56 = 12 minutes. 60 + 12 = 72 minutes. On Bus B the journey takes 11:39 to 12:39 = 60 minutes plus 12:39 to 12:48 = 9 minutes. 60 + 9 = 69 minutes. The journey on Bus A is longer, so the longest time is 72 minutes.

16. A

When you multiply two odd numbers together you always make an odd number. So 113 × 115 will give an odd number as the answer.

17. A

The mode is the most popular result. Silver, purple and blue were each chosen once, gold and green were each chosen twice but red was chosen three times, so red is the mode.

18. 9

Ester won 32 prizes altogether so subtract the number she won on the other days from 32 to find the number she won on Thursday: 32 – 5 – 8 – 4 – 6 = 9

19. D
Look at each statement and decide if it's true:
A: $\frac{3}{4} = \frac{75}{100}$, so $\frac{7}{100}$ isn't greater than $\frac{3}{4}$.
B: $\frac{7}{100} = 0.07$, so $\frac{7}{100}$ isn't greater than 0.65.
C: $\frac{7}{100} = 0.07$, so $\frac{7}{100}$ isn't greater than 0.09.
D: $\frac{3}{4} = 0.75$, so 0.65 is less than $\frac{3}{4}$.
E: 0.65 is greater than 0.09.

20. B
The cactus plants come in boxes of 12 and Lemone needs 60 plants so she needs $60 \div 12 = 5$ boxes. The cost of 5 boxes is shown in the expression as $5C$. She needs to add this to the cost of the stall, S, so the complete expression is $S + 5C$.

21. 2
The total angle around the point at the centre of the spinner is 360° and there are 8 sections, so the size of each section is $360° \div 8 = 45°$. $360° - 45° = 315°$ so the arrow is being turned in an anti-clockwise direction through 7 segments $(8 - 1 = 7)$ which will leave it pointing at number 2.

22. D
$25 \times 4 = 100$, so it takes 4 days to run 100 miles. The number of days to run 800 miles will be $4 \times 8 = 32$ days. This leaves 74 miles left over. $25 \times 3 = 75$ so it'll take 3 days to complete the last 74 miles. 32 days + 3 days = 35 days

23. 6 cm²
You can work out the area of a rectangle by finding length × width. So, the area of the flag is $6 \times 4 = 24$ cm². The flag is split into 4 equal rectangles, so the area of the shaded rectangle is $24 \div 4 = 6$ cm²

24. D
46 is 23 doubled, so 46×14 is 23×14 doubled. So $46 \times 14 = 322 \times 2 = 644$ 140 is 10 times larger than 14, so $46 \times 140 = 644 \times 10 = 6440$ sweets

25. 24
The probability of Penny picking a white sock from the drawer is $\frac{2}{3}$. This means $\frac{2}{3}$ of the socks are white. There are 36 socks in total, so the number of white socks is $\frac{2}{3}$ of 36. $\frac{1}{3}$ of $36 = 36 \div 3 = 12$ So $\frac{2}{3}$ of 36 is $2 \times 12 = 24$ socks

26. D
n is the number of the term. Test each formula by substituting different values for n. E.g for option D: $n - (n + 1)$: When n is 1: $1 - (1 + 1) = 1 - 2 = -1$. When n is 2: $2 - (2 + 1) = 2 - 3 = -1$. When n is 3: $3 - (3 + 1) = 3 - 4 = -1$. So $n - (n + 1)$ is the correct formula.

27. C
For Julie to have shared the carrots equally, whilst having none left over and not having to divide any, the number of rabbits must be a factor of the number of carrots, 70. The only factor of 70 is 5 $(70 \div 5 = 14)$.

28. D
Four squares north takes Adam to $(-1, 2)$. Two squares east takes him to $(1, 2)$.

29. D
$3(p + 6t)$ means: $p + 6t + p + 6t + p + 6t = 3p + 18t$

30. 68%
To find a percentage you need to write an equivalent fraction over 100. $\frac{16}{50}$ people had a blue car and when you multiply the numerator and denominator in $\frac{16}{50}$ by 2 you get $\frac{32}{100} = 32\%$. The percentage of people who didn't have a blue car is $100\% - 32\% = 68\%$

Section B
Pages 56-58

1. C
Add the prices of the sets of three board games together. You need to find the option that adds up to £30.00 – £0.50 = £29.50. This is easiest if you split the numbers and add the pounds and pence separately. Blocks + Clueless + Trivia Time = £12.50 + £6.50 + £10.50 = £12 + £6 + £10 + £0.50 + £0.50 + £0.50 = £28 + £1.50 = £29.50

2. £9.50
Two copies of Brainium cost £9.50 × 2 = £19. Three copies of Trivia Time cost £10.50 × 3 = £31.50 Together they cost £19 + £31.50 = £50.50 Jill paid with 3 × £20 = £60. The change she received was £60 – £50.50 = £9.50

3. 50 cm²
The area of each square is length × width = 4 × 4 = 16 cm². The area of $\frac{1}{2}$ a square = 16 ÷ 2 = 8 cm². 1 whole square + 3 halves = 16 + 8 + 8 + 8 = 40 cm² She uses 2 half circles so 1 circle in total. The total area of the circle is 10 cm². So, the total area is 40 + 10 = 50 cm²

4. 4 m
The area of each tile is 0.04 m² and Moses uses 100 tiles to cover the floor, so the total area of the bathroom is 100 × 0.04 = 4 m². The area of the bathroom is calculated using length × width, so area ÷ width = length: 4 ÷ 1 = 4 m

5. 11 : 9
White tiles occupy 55% of the floor while black tiles cover 45%. Written as a ratio this is 55 : 45. The highest common factor of 55 and 45 is 5. Dividing both sides by 5 gives the ratio in its simplest form, 11 : 9.

6. 1.8 m²
The total area of the bathroom is 4 m². 10% of the overall area is 4 ÷ 10 = 0.4 m² and 5% of the overall area is 0.4 ÷ 2 = 0.2 m² Therefore 45% of the total area is $(0.4 \times 4) + 0.2 = 1.6 + 0.2 = 1.8$ m².

7. 120°
Each angle in an equilateral triangle is 60°. The shaded angle is made up of the angles from two equilateral triangles so it is $60° + 60° = 120°$

8. 12
In total, the girls have $H + (H + 2) + 2H$ handbags. If they have 26 handbags altogether, this can be written as: $26 = H + (H + 2) + 2H$. This is simplified to: $26 = 4H + 2$. Subtract 2 from both sides: $24 = 4H$ So $H = 24 \div 4$, so $H = 6$. Louise has $2H$ handbags. $2 \times 6 = 12$ handbags.

9. C
Amy has $H + 2$ handbags. Georgina has 3 times this. $(H + 2) + (H + 2) + (H + 2) = 3H + 6$

10. 91
£2.73 is made up evenly of 2p and 1p coins. 1p out of every 3p is a 1p coin, so $\frac{1}{3}$ of the money is made up from 1p coins. £2.73 is 273p and $\frac{1}{3}$ of 273 is 273 ÷ 3 = 91. So, 91 coins are 1p coins.

11. 30

	Girls	Boys	Total
Goals		4	
Saves	14	= (20 – 4) = 16	= (16 + 14) = **30**
Total	24	= (44 – 24) = 20	44

The table shows how to find the total number of saves. Start by working out the boys' total goals and saves (20). Then use this to find the number of the boys' saves (16). Add this to the girls' saves to find the total number of saves (30).

12. 5000
The length of each matchbox is 5 cm. This will fit along one side of the box 50 × 5 = 10 times. The width of each matchbox is 2 cm. This will fit along one side of the box 50 × 2 = 25 times. So one layer of matchboxes = 10 × 25 = 250 matchboxes. The height of each matchbox is 1 cm, so the box is high enough to fit 20 ÷ 1 = 20 layers of matchboxes in it. So the total number of matchboxes = 20 × 250 = 5000

13. 125 000
In question 12, it was calculated that there were 5000 matchboxes in the packing box. If there are 25 matches in each match box, there are 5000 × 25 matches in the packing box in total. You can calculate this by finding 25 × 1000 × 5. 25 × 1000 = 25 000, 25 000 × 5 = 125 000.

14. £16
The cost of tickets for 2 adults and 2 children is £3.50 + £3.50 + £1.50 + £1.50 = £10 A family ticket is 20% cheaper — 10% of £10 is £1 so 20% is £2. So a family ticket is £10 – £2 = £8 Raj is buying two family tickets so the total cost is £8 × 2 = £16

15. 5
The number of sausage rolls eaten by the children is 24 × 3 = 72 and the number eaten by the adults is 7 × 5 = 35. So the total number of sausage rolls eaten is 72 + 35 = 107. The sausage rolls come in packets of 25. 4 × 25 = 100 so Sherrie will need to buy 5 packets to have 107 sausage rolls.

16. 4
There are 7 adults who eat $\frac{1}{7}$ of a cake each. $7 \times \frac{1}{7} = 1$ cake There are 24 children who eat $\frac{1}{8}$ of a cake each. $24 \times \frac{1}{8} = 24 \div 8 = 3$ cakes In total Sherrie needs 1 + 3 = 4 cakes

17. 10 years
The plant needs to grow 0.5 m (2 – 1.5 = 0.5). It grows 0.025 m in 6 months. There are 12 months in a year so it will grow 0.025 × 2 = 0.05 m in a year. 0.5 m ÷ 0.05 m = 10, so it'll take the plant 10 years to grow 0.5 m.

18. 9 m
The vertical sides of the shape measure 1 + 6 + 7 = 14 m. So, the total of the horizontal sides of the shape is 32 – 14 = 18 m. The bottom horizontal line is equal to the 2 top sides added together so the bottom horizontal line is half of the remaining perimeter. The length of X (the bottom) is 18 ÷ 2 = 9 m.

19. 58 m²
Area of a rectangle = width × height. The house can be split up into two rectangles.

The bottom rectangle has an area of 6 × 9 = 54 m² The upper rectangle has an area of 4 × 1 = 4 m² The total area is 54 + 4 = 58 m²

20. 25%
The total amount of paint used by Harry is 3 + 4 + 5 = 12 litres. 3 litres of this was red paint, so the fraction of red paint used is $\frac{3}{12}$. $\frac{3}{12}$ is simplified to $\frac{1}{4}$ by dividing the numerator and denominator by 3, and $\frac{1}{4} = 25\%$ (25% × 4 = 100%).

21. D

The diagram shows the flag when it has been rotated clockwise by 90° about (0, 0). The coordinates of point P are now (3, −3).

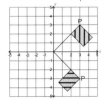

22. B

n is the number of the term. To find the first term, substitute 1 for n in the expression $3n^2 + 1$ (remember to follow BODMAS):
$3 \times 1^2 + 1 = 3 \times 1 + 1 = 3 + 1 = 4$
To find the second term, n is 2:
$3 \times 2^2 + 1 = 3 \times 4 + 1 = 12 + 1 = 13$

23. 12 cm³

The volume of each cube of cheese is $2 \times 2 \times 2 = 8\ cm^3$.
There are 3 cubes of cheese, so the total volume of cheese is $8 \times 3 = 24\ cm^3$.
The mouse eats $12\ cm^3$ of cheese, so the amount left is $24 - 12 = 12\ cm^3$

24. D

The regular pentagon has 5 sides that are all $(2x - y)$ m.
$5(2x - y) = 2x - y + 2x - y + 2x - y + 2x - y$
$\qquad\qquad\quad + 2x - y = 10x - 5y$

25. 90 m

You can substitute the values $x = 10$ and $y = 2$ into the expression from question 24.
$10 \times 10 - 5 \times 2 = 100 - 10 = 90$ m
Alternatively, substitute the values of x and y into the expression for one side of the pen
$2 \times 10 - 2 = 20 - 2 = 18$ m
There are 5 sides to the pen so the total perimeter is $18 \times 5 = 90$ m

26. 33

Brian needs $50\ m^2$ for every 3 sheep.
You need to work out how many lots of $50\ m^2$ there are in $555\ m^2$.
$555 \div 50 = 11$ remainder 5. For every $50\ m^2$ Brian can have 3 sheep. Since there are only 11 full lots of $50\ m^2$, Brian can fit $11 \times 3 = 33$ sheep in the pen. There is a remainder of $5\ m^2$ which is not big enough for one sheep.

27. 136°

A kite is a quadrilateral so the angles in a kite add up 360°. This means that the angle missing in the kite is $360° - 130° - 130° - 56° = 44°$
Angles on a straight line add up to 180°, so angle a is $180° - 44° = 136°$

28. C

Round up 49p to 50p and 29p to 30p to make the calculations easier. Carrie bought 4 chocolate bars so the approximate price of these is $4 \times 50p = £2$. She bought 7 bags of peanuts so the approximate price of these is $7 \times 30p = £2.10$.
$£2 + £2.10 = £4.10$. You rounded each item up by 1p and there were 11 items in total $(4 + 7 = 11)$ so subtract 11p to find the exact total cost: $£4.10 - 11p = £3.99$

29. 8 hours

Start by making sure everything is in the same units — there were 2 litres of water, so change this to millilitres by multiplying by 1000: $2 \times 1000 = 2000$ ml. There are 5 holes each losing 50 ml each hour, so the amount of water being lost each hour is $5 \times 50 = 250$ ml. Divide the total volume of water (2000) by the amount being lost each hour (250) to find the number of hours it'll take to empty: $2000 \div 250 = 8$ hours

30. 120 minutes

If one hole is stoppered then only $4 \times 50 = 200$ ml of water will be lost per hour. $2000 \div 200 = 10$ hours. This is $10 - 8 = 2$ hours more than when all 5 holes are losing water. 2 hours is $60 \times 2 = 120$ minutes.

Assessment Test 3

Section A
Pages 59-61

1. 6.5 cm²

The area of a whole square is $1\ cm^2$, so the area of half a square is $0.5\ cm^2$. There are 5 whole squares with an area of $5 \times 1\ cm^2 = 5\ cm^2$, and 3 half squares with an area of $3 \times 0.5\ cm^2 = 1.5\ cm^2$, so the total area is $5 + 1.5 = 6.5\ cm^2$

2. C

Litres is not a unit of length. Centimetres and millimetres are too small. Kilometres are too big. So metres is the most suitable unit.

3. 7

Each rectangle represents 4 vehicles, so ¼ of a rectangle represents 1 vehicle.
There are 1¾ rectangles for the buses.
This is equivalent to 4 buses for the whole rectangle and 3 buses for the ¾ rectangle.
$3 + 4 = 7$ buses

4. 6

The children with a skateboard and a scooter are shown in the overlap of the skateboard and scooter circles. The 1 child in the middle section also has a bike, so you don't want to count that one.

5. E

E (a trapezium) is the only shape with one pair of parallel sides (the top and bottom). A and B have more than one pair of parallel sides. C and D have no parallel sides.

6. A

In the 24 hour clock, if the number of hours is greater than 12, the time is pm. To convert from the 24-hour clock to the 12-hour clock subtract 12 from the hours, in this case, 13. $13 - 12 = 1$. So the answer is 1:45 pm.

7. D

There are eight lines of symmetry:

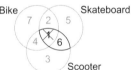

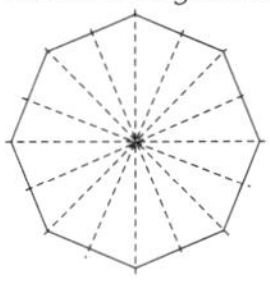

8. 113

Add up the number of boys and girls in each year:
Year 2: $49 + 50 = 99$
Year 3: $52 + 56 = 108$
Year 4: $55 + 57 = 112$
Year 5: $54 + 59 = 113$
Year 6: $35 + 54 = 89$
Year 5 is the biggest year group and has 113 children.

9. 7.2

0.08 is 1000 times smaller than 80, so 90×0.08 will be 1000 times smaller than 90×80. $90 \times 80 = 7200$, so $90 \times 0.08 = 7200 \div 1000 = 7.2$

10. B

400 g is the only sensible answer. 4 kg and 40 kg are too big. 4 g and 0.4 g are too small.

11. C

Total up the 3 items Maddy chose and subtract the total from £5.00.
$40p + 25p + 99p = £1.64$ (to add on 99p, add on £1 and subtract 1p).
$£5.00 - £1.64 = £3.36$

12. B

Convert all the fractions to twentieths so they're easier to put in order:
$\frac{3}{4} = \frac{15}{20}$ *(Multiply the numerator and denominator by 5.)*
$\frac{1}{5} = \frac{4}{20}$ *(Multiply the numerator and denominator by 4.)*
The other three fractions are already in twentieths. In order from smallest to largest, the fractions are:
$\frac{3}{20}, \frac{4}{20}, \frac{5}{20}, \frac{7}{20}, \frac{15}{20}$
Convert the fractions back to their original form to give: $\frac{3}{20}, \frac{1}{5}, \frac{5}{20}, \frac{7}{20}, \frac{3}{4}$

13. 12

From the chart, you can see that 70% of children in the computer club are boys.
There are 30 children in the club, so find 70% of 30.
10% of 30 = $30 \div 10 = 3$
so 70% = $7 \times 10\% = 7 \times 3 = 21$.
There must be $30 - 21 = 9$ girls.
So there are $21 - 9 = 12$ more boys than girls.

14. C

The fastest time is the smallest number. Cara was fastest with 3 mins 59 secs. All the other times are over 4 minutes so compare the seconds. Ian came second with a time of 4 mins 2 secs.

15. 11

To find the answer you need to work backwards from 112. You're told that 9 was subtracted from a number to make 112 — so add 9 to 112: $112 + 9 = 121$. To reach 121 the original number was multiplied by 11. So you need to divide 121 by 11 to find the original number: $121 \div 11 = 11$

16. D

The numbers above 4 on a dice are 5 and 6. This is 2 out of the 6 numbers, so the probability is $\frac{2}{6} = \frac{1}{3}$

17. E

The map below shows Jenny's movements. Remember — 90° is a right angle, so 135° is one and a half right angles $(90° + 45°)$.

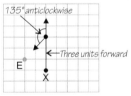

18. 6:05 pm

1¾ hours = 1 hour 45 mins.
Count on 1 hour and 45 mins from 4:20 pm. One hour later than 4:20 pm is 5:20 pm, 40 minutes later than 5:20 pm is 6:00 pm, 5 minutes later than 6:00 pm is 6:05 pm.
Alternatively, 1¾ hours is 15 minutes less than 2 hours. So you could add on 2 hours and then subtract 15 minutes.

19. 2 km

Sarah runs on $7 \times 12 = 84$ days
Each day she runs $168 \div 84 = 2$ km.

20. C

You need to imagine spinning the shape round to different positions. This question is easier if you rotate the page so that the cube with the heart is at the top each time.

21. 20 cm

The perimeter of a rectangle is made up of 2 lengths and 2 widths. In this rectangle,
length = width + 20 cm, so the perimeter is
2 widths + 2 widths + 20 cm + 20 cm
= 4 widths + 40 cm
The perimeter is 120 cm, so 4 widths is
120 cm – 40 cm = 80 cm
So 1 width is 80 cm ÷ 4 = 20 cm

22. 2.25 °C

The highest temperature was 38.25 °C on Saturday. The lowest temperature was 36 °C on Monday and Wednesday.
So the range = 38.25 – 36 = 2.25 °C

23. E

Count up from –5 in steps of 1.5 until you land on one of the answer choices.
–5, –3.5, –2, –0.5, 1, 2.5, 4 (which is E).

24. B

The pattern is made by repeating a set of three shapes.
3 × 6 = 18, so there will be 6 full sets of the shapes, plus another two that make up the first 20 shapes. The heart is the 1st shape in the pattern, so shape 19 will be a heart.
So there will be 6 + 1 = 7 hearts

25. 597 miles

If Sue can travel 2985 miles on 5 tanks, she can travel 2985 ÷ 5 miles on 1 tank: 5)2⁹9⁴8³5 = 0 5 9 7

26. 31

You could do this question by predicting what the 11th shape will look like and counting the squares. Shape 11 will have a vertical strip of 11 squares, and the horizontal strips sticking out the sides will be 10 squares long each. The total number of squares will be 11 + 10 + 10 = 31
Alternatively, you could say that the number of squares increases by 3 each time. There are 10 squares in Shape 4, and Shape 11 is 7 shapes further on.
So Shape 11 will have 7 × 3 = 21 more squares than Shape 4.
This means it has 10 + 21 = 31 in total.

27. 11

1.75 pints = 1 litre, so 6 litres = 6 × 1.75 pints. Split the calculation up to make it easier.
2 litres = 2 × 1.75 = 3.5 pints
6 litres = 3 × 2 litres, so:
6 litres = 3 × 3.5 = 10.5 pints
So you'd need 11 bottles.

28. B

Consider whether each statement is true:
A: There are 4 even numbers and only 2 odd, so this isn't true.
B: 3 numbers out of 6 are greater than 4, so the probability of it landing on one of them is even. The statement is true.
C: There are 6 equal sections, and so each number has a ⅙ chance of being spun. So the statement isn't true.
D: More than half the numbers are even, so the probability of an even number being spun can't be ⅓. So the statement isn't true.
E: There are only two numbers less than 3. This is less than half of the possible numbers, so the probability of one of them being spun can't be a half.

29. D

First find what fraction of the bottle she has used by simplifying: ¹²⁵⁄₅₀₀ = ²⁵⁄₁₀₀ = ¼.
Then find what fraction of the bottle of shampoo is left: 1 – ¼ = ¾

30. (8, 2)

The fourth corner is directly below the point (8, 10) so it will have the same x-coordinate (8).
It is directly to the right of the point (4, 2) so it will have the same y-coordinate (2).

So the coordinates of the missing corner are (8, 2).

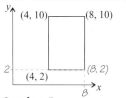

Section B
Pages 62-64

1. D

The reflected point is the same distance away from the mirror line on both sides.

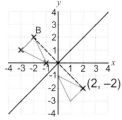

2. C

Write out the four given ages in order: 2, 3, 6, 8. For the median age to stay the same, 3 and 6 have to remain the middle two values. So one of the missing ages must be 3 or less, and the other must be 6 or more. This means that the correct answer must be C (2 and 8).

3. B

The whole pie chart represents 20 days.
If 20 days = 360°, then 1 day = 360° ÷ 20 = 18°
3 foggy days will be represented by an angle of 3 × 18° = 54°

4. 6

From question 3, one day is represented by 18°. Therefore 108° corresponds to 108 ÷ 18 = 6 days (as 54 ÷ 18 = 3 and 108 is double 54).

5. 26

A cube has 6 faces, 12 edges and 8 vertices (corners). 6 + 12 + 8 = 26.
If you don't know these, you could count them on the diagram in the question.

6. 6 cm

This can be done using trial and error. To calculate the length of one edge, the cube root of 216 needs to be found:
4 × 4 × 4 = 64
5 × 5 × 5 = 125
6 × 6 × 6 = 216

7. £50

Substitute 300 for m in the formula and find C. Remember to follow BODMAS.
C = 15(300 ÷ 100) + 5
C = 15(3) + 5
C = 45 + 5
C = 50
The cost of printing 300 leaflets is £50.

8. B

There are 1000 ml in 1 litre, so in 10 litres, there are 10 000 ml.
⅖ of a litre = ²⁄₅ × 1000 ml = (1000 × 2) ÷ 5 = 2000 ÷ 5 = 400 ml
So the amount left in the bucket = 10 000 – 400 = 9600 ml

9. 4.5 kg

7.5 kg of rabbit flakes are used which corresponds to 5 parts. So one part is 7.5 ÷ 5 = 1.5 kg. There needs to be 3 parts of hay, so 1.5 × 3 = 4.5 kg is needed.

---

10. 31.5 kg

There are 1 + 3 + 5 = 9 parts in the mix and vegetables only make up 1 part of it.
There are 3.5 kg of vegetables in the mix and so the total weight is 3.5 × 9. Split this up into 3 × 9 = 27 and 0.5 × 9 = 4.5 and add them together, 27 + 4.5 = 31.5 kg.

11. 95

The number of children can be found by identifying the correct bar (the darker grey bar) and reading off the values on the y-axis.
On Monday 30 children used the ferry.
On Tuesday 40 children used the ferry.
On Wednesday 25 children used the ferry.
In total on the first three days:
30 + 40 + 25 = 95 children used the ferry.

12. 40

To work out the number of passengers that used the ferry in one day, add the totals of both the adult and children bars.
Monday: 15 + 30 = 45 passengers
Tuesday: 25 + 40 = 65 passengers
Wednesday: 10 + 25 = 35 passengers
Thursday: 30 + 15 = 45 passengers
Friday: 10 + 55 = 65 passengers
Saturday: 35 + 35 = 70 passengers
Sunday: 40 + 35 = 75 passengers
The highest number of passengers in one day is on Sunday (75) and the fewest is on Wednesday (35). The range is therefore 75 – 35 = 40 passengers

13. D

On Thursday 30 adults and 15 children used the ferry. 15 is half of 30.

14. 35

On both Saturday and Sunday, 35 children used the ferry.

15. 210

The calculation is easier if you notice that 11 + 12 + 13 + 14 + 15 + 16 + 17 + 18 + 19 + 20 is the same as (1 + 2 + 3 + 4 + 5 + 6 + 7 + 8 + 9 + 10) + (10 × 10). You are told in the question that the sum of the numbers from 1 to 10 is 55. So the total = 55 + 55 + 100 = 210

16. 8

The prime numbers between 1 and 20 are: 2, 3, 5, 7, 11, 13, 17 and 19.

17. B

The minute hand will go round 10.5 times between 12 noon and 10:30 pm. It travels through 360° each time it goes round. So the total angle it travels through is 10.5 × 360°. Split this up into 10 × 360° = 3600° and 0.5 × 360° = 180°, then add them up: 3600° + 180° = 3780°

18. £9.75

Find 30% of £2.50: 10% of £2.50 = £0.25 30% = 3 × 10% = 3 × £0.25 = £0.75 So if he cleans the car one week he gets £2.50 + £0.75 = £3.25 So for 3 weeks he gets £3.25 × 3 = £9.75

19. 52 m²

First find the area of the whole garden, then subtract the area of the flower bed. This gives you the lawn area.
Garden = 8 × 8 = 64 m²
Flower bed = 4 × 3 = 12 m²
Lawn = 64 – 12 = 52 m²

20. 1 hour 5 minutes

In question 19, it was calculated that the lawn is 52 m². It takes Tamara 5 minutes to mow 4 m² of lawn. In 52 m² there are 52 ÷ 4 = 13 lots of 4 m². It will take Tamara 5 × 13 = 65 minutes to mow the lawn.
This is equivalent to 1 hour and 5 minutes.

21. B

Ian has rounded each item up by 1p. There are 9 items, so his estimate will be 9p too much.